INTERNATIONAL BANK FOR RECONSTRUCTION AND DEVELOPMENT

WORLD BANK STAFF OCCASIONAL PAPERS NUMBER SEVEN

MAP 1

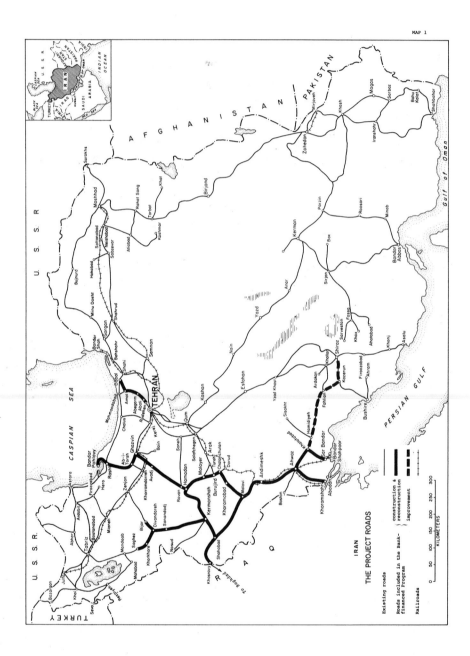

IRAN

THE PROJECT ROADS

Existing roads

Roads included in the Bank-financed Program { construction & reconstruction, improvement

Railroads

0 50 100 150 200 250 300
KILOMETERS

HERMAN G. VAN DER TAK and JAN DE WEILLE

REAPPRAISAL
OF A ROAD PROJECT
IN IRAN

Distributed by The Johns Hopkins Press
Baltimore, Maryland

FOREWORD

I would like to explain *why* the World Bank Group does research work, and why it publishes it. We feel an obligation to look beyond the projects we help to finance toward the whole resource allocation of an economy, and the effectiveness of the use of those resources. Our major concern, in dealings with member countries, is that all scarce resources, including capital, skilled labor, enterprise and know-how, should be used to their best advantage. We want to see policies that encourage appropriate increases in the supply of savings, whether domestic or international. Finally, we are required by our Articles, as well as by inclination, to use objective economic criteria in all our judgments.

These are our preoccupations, and these, one way or another, are the subjects of most of our research work. Clearly, they are also the proper concerns of anyone who is interested in promoting development, and so we seek to make our research papers widely available. In doing so, we have to take the risk of being misunderstood. Although these studies are published by the Bank, the views expressed and the methods explored should not necessarily be considered to represent the Bank's views or policies. Rather they are offered as a modest contribution to the great discussion on how to advance the economic development of the underdeveloped world.

ROBERT S. MCNAMARA
President
International Bank for
Reconstruction and Development

v

TABLE OF CONTENTS

PREFACE   xiii

I. INTRODUCTION   1
    The Project   3
    Outline of Chapters   3

II. BACKGROUND AND HISTORY OF THE
    PROJECT   5
    The Pattern of Economic Activity   5
    Modes of Transportation   6
    The Roads Program in the First and Second Plans   6
    The Project   9
        Description   9
        Execution   11
        Total Cost   14
    The Question of Priorities   14

III. ANALYSIS OF CONSTRUCTION COSTS
AND SCHEDULES   19
     Original Estimates and Actual Costs   19
     Reasons for Cost Increases Given in Progress
         Reports   20
     Analysis of Reasons for Cost Increases   22
     Delays in Construction   26
     Reasons Given by the Consultants   29

IV. ADDITIONAL COST INFORMATION   31
     Typical Construction Costs   31
     Stage Construction   34
     Road Maintenance   36

V. TRAFFIC STRUCTURE AND GROWTH   41
     Estimating the Volume of Traffic   42
     The Traffic Counts   42
     The Weighing Stations   44
     Truck Traffic Diverted from Rail   45
     Traffic Growth   47
     Future Growth of Traffic   49

VI. ROAD USER SAVINGS AND TRUCKING RATES   53
     Road User Costs and Savings   54
     Average Year-Round Costs   55
     Changes in Trucking Rates   58
     Truck and Rail Rates   61
     Associated Cost Savings   62

VII. DEVELOPMENT BENEFITS   65
     Agricultural Benefits   66
     Possible Impact of Marketing System   69

VIII. COST-BENEFIT ANALYSIS OF THE PROJECT   75
     Basic Costs and Benefit Data   76
     Cost-Benefit Comparisons   80
     Alternative Assumptions and Estimates   84
     Alternative Investments   86
     Concluding Remarks   88

IX. CONCLUSIONS AND RECOMMENDATIONS 89
   Conclusions 89
     Construction Cost Increases and Construction Delays 89
     Typical Construction Costs 89
     Stage Construction 90
     Maintenance Costs 90
     Traffic Data 90
     Diversion from Railways 91
     Vehicle Registration, Fuel Consumption and Future Growth of Traffic 91
     Road User Savings and Rate Reductions 91
     Average Year-Round Trucking Costs and Rates 92
     Rail and Truck Rates 92
     Development Benefits 92
     Cost-Benefit Analysis 93
     Sensitivity Analysis 93
     Influence of Increases in Construction Costs 93
     Need for Comprehensive Analysis 94
     Deficiencies of Data 94
   Recommendations 94
     Data Collection 94
     Project Appraisal 95
     Follow-Up 97
   Present-day Practice of the Bank 97

ANNEXES

I Additional Traffic Information and Reliability of Traffic Data 99
II Road User Savings and Year-Round Costs 113

TABLES

1. Roads under Maintenance by the Ministry of Roads in Iran, 1957–1965 9
2. Main Road Program 10
3. Actual Construction and Consultants' Costs of Main Roads in the Project 21

4. Construction Costs, by Road, according to the Consultants   23

5. Construction Cost Increases, by Category of Lot   24

6. Analysis of Consultants' Costs   26

7. Comparison of Construction Delays and Cost Increases by Category of Lot   29

8. Reason for Delay in Work   30

9. Typical Construction Cost per km in Iran, 1965   32

10. Cost of Paving a Road by Stages   35

11. Annual Maintenance Cost by Type of Road, Data from Three Sources   36

12. Typical Road Construction and Consultants' Costs in Iran, 1965—Mountainous Terrain   38

13. Typical Road Construction and Consultants' Costs in Iran, 1965—Normal Terrain   39

14. Typical Road Construction and Consultants' Costs in Iran, 1965—Flat or Rolling Terrain   40

15. Traffic Count Information on the Project Roads, 1960–1962   43

16. Imports Transported from Khoramshahr and Bandar Shahpoor, by Rail and Road, 1959–1964   46

17. Vehicle Registration, 1958–1963   47

18. Fuel Consumption, 1958–1964   48

19. Imports by Commodity Groups, Volume and Value, 1963   50

20. Summary of Road User Costs and Savings, 1965 (excluding taxes)   55

21. Comparison of Average Trucking and Road User Costs   58

22. Trucking Rates, Khoramshahr–Tehran, 1961–65   59

23. Sample Trucking Rates, Khoramshahr–Tehran, 1958–60   60

24. Comparison of Road and Rail Rates   62

25. Interest Savings Related to Transit Time   64

26. Wholesale Price Differentials between Tehran and Selected Market Towns, 1960–64   69

27. Farm Wholesale and Retail Prices, 1961 and 1962   72

28. Total Costs (Construction and Consultants') of the Road Project, by Road and Over Time   77

29. Description of the Project Roads before and after Reconstruction and Completion Dates   78

30.	Road User Savings by Type of Vehicle and Road Improvement	79
31.	Unit Cost Savings by Road	80
32.	Discounted Costs and Benefits of the Project Roads per Kilometer	83
33.	Discounted Net Benefits, Total Road Sections, Present Value in 1962	84

CHARTS

1.	Iran: Originally Scheduled and Actual Construction Periods	28
2.	Iran: Road User Costs and Savings, 1965	57
3.	Benefits of a Road Project	67
4.	Iran: Costs and Benefits of the Project Roads	81
5.	Northbound Heavy Truck Traffic, 1964	104

MAPS

1.	The Project Roads	*Frontispiece*
2.	The Project Roads as Numbered in this Study	12
3.	The Location of the Weighing Stations	101

ANNEX TABLES

1.	North and Southbound Truck Traffic on the Roads Adjacent to Ahwaz, 1961 and 1964	102
2.	Northbound Flow of Freight on the Trans-Iranian Highway, 1964	106
3.	Composition of Transport Flow, 1964	107
4.	Alternative Estimates of the Volume of Transport from Khoramshahr Northbound, 1961 and 1964	110
5.	Road User Costs and Savings, excluding taxes, per Vehicle by Road Surface, Iran, 1965	114
6.	Prices, 1965 and 1960, including and excluding Taxes	116
7.	Road User Savings, at 1960 Prices, including Taxes	120
8.	Road User Savings per Capacity Ton-km, excluding Taxes	121
9.	Average Year-Round Trucking Costs, Iran, 1965	122
10.	Trucking Rates between Various Towns, 1965	125
11.	Relationship of Load Factor to Profit	126

Definitions

Dollars ($) are US dollars equivalent, converted at current par values. During the period, we have taken US$1 = Rials 75, Rials 100 = US$1.33.

Notations

  .. not available

  — nil or negligible

It has been Bank policy to withhold internal documents from public distribution. Accordingly, these documents are not described by their full titles in this study.

Because of rounding, sum totals in tables may not be exact.

PREFACE

This study originated in a decision by the World Bank to make a more systematic effort to evaluate the actual economic effects of projects for which the Bank has made loans. The Bank of course has an intrinsic interest in the success or failure of projects. Beyond this interest, it was expected that economic reappraisals of projects would enable the Bank to improve its own techniques of project analysis and appraisal. And just as important, it was believed that a project reappraisal would be distilled experience which would be of substantial value to the Bank's member countries in their development planning.

For various reasons, road transport was felt to be a particularly rewarding field for this kind of inquiry. The roster of road projects suitable for reappraisal proved more limited than had been envisaged. Within the small group of projects found acceptable, the ultimate choice of Project 227 IRN was to some extent arbitrary. A final factor in its favor was the assurance of cooperation by the Iranian authorities.

Following preparatory work in Washington, the authors visited Iran for varying periods during April/May 1965. Mr. Alf Bergan of the Bank's Transportation Projects Department acted as their technical adviser during the early part of their stay in Iran and was consulted during the analytical phase. Mr. Jochen K. Schmedtje, of the Bank's Western Africa Department, participated in the field work and wrote an early draft of Chapter II. Mr. Hyung M. Kim assisted in the analysis of statistical material.

The authors received cordial cooperation and assistance from many sources, their colleagues in the Bank, in particular Mr. Warren Baum, of the Projects Department, Mr. Hans Adler, of the Programming and Budgeting Department, and Mr. Sei-Young Park, of the Transportation Projects Department, and many people in private and public life in Iran who unstintingly gave them the benefit of their advice, knowledge and experience. In many cases this went far beyond a willingness to discuss matters and problems relating to the study; considerable effort went into assembling and rearranging relevant material, and the Bank is appreciative of the burden undertaken on its behalf. Gratitude is also extended to the Ministry of Roads for collecting data on truck transport from registers kept by the weighing stations, and to the consultants supervising the project for detailed information on construction costs and delays. Other examples will be found throughout this study. The mission was fortunate also to have its task facilitated by efficient working arrangements made by the Plan Organization, including hospitable quarters in the Organization's offices. Without this manifold help the study could not have been written. The authors alone, however, are responsible for the presentation and interpretation of facts.

The art of project appraisal is subject to progressive evolution. The original appraisal report of the project discussed in this study is nearly ten years old. In a number of respects therefore it is not representative of present-day Bank appraisal practice.

This staff study is part of continuing work in the Economics Department on problems of sector and project analysis. It has a particular practical value in demonstrating the use in a specific country of the data collected in *Quantification of Road User Savings*— the second paper in this series.

Andrew M. Kamarck
Director
Economics Department

xiv

I

INTRODUCTION

An economic reappraisal of a project attempts, after the project has been implemented, to assess its economic costs and benefits. These actual costs and benefits can then be compared to the original figures on which the investment decision was based. It may be possible to identify factors responsible for differences between expectation and results.

Such a case study can lead to broader insights. On the basis of several studies it may become possible to identify factors which are crucial to the success or failure of a particular type of project. Reappraisal may also lead to a better conceptual framework for project evaluation, and in particular to better ways of assessing costs and benefits.

The limitations of economic reappraisal studies should be clearly understood. Although the passage of time provides a vantage point for looking at costs and benefits, an economic end-use study will only in rare instances, if ever, be able to survey the history of a project over its full economic life. In most cases the studies will be undertaken, say, five to ten years or less after the project is completed. Construction costs can be ascertained soon after construction is finished. But a large part, if not most, of the benefits will remain hidden in the future. Similarly, supplementary investment costs and operating and maintenance costs—both necessary for deriving total net benefits of the project—may not be definitely known. Thus evaluation of costs as well as benefits, while becoming easier with the passage of time, remains subject to projection and conjecture.

Another limitation is that even if the project's results have become available in their entirety, it is difficult to isolate the specific effects of the project on the economic life of the community. A reappraisal should be based on a comparison of costs and benefits "with" and "without" the project. Increases in output or in traffic may have occurred after the road was built, but not necessarily because of it. Again, even with a completely accurate analysis of development "with" the project, the problem remains to determine what would have happened "without" it.

In sum, project analysis is much more than a matter of investigating actual events. Project analysis, both before the project is undertaken and in hindsight, is an intellectual construction—costs and benefits have to be constructed from a mixture of empirical and conjectural data, within an appropriate analytical framework.

This particular study suffers from some specific limitations of data. Although the Iranian road project qualified in terms of the study team's basic requirements—with regard to completion date, available information before and after construction, the quality of *ex ante* analysis and other relevant considerations—the data base, as it turned out, was very weak in some important aspects. The authors have made a considerable effort to use all available information, even where this required reconstructing or processing "raw" data; they have employed statistical precautions to ensure, so far as possible, the internal consistency of the data. They did not, however, organize special inquiries such as traffic counts. Some of the deficiencies could undoubtedly have been overcome by generating fresh data. In fact, one of the conclusions of this study is that road reappraisal technique could be improved by setting up special inquiries in good time. Whatever its deficiencies, the authors believe that the present study contributes to practical research in a field which has only recently begun to receive the attention it deserves.[1]

---

[1] The only road project reappraisals which have been published, so far as the authors are aware, are included in the volume by George W. Wilson, Barbara R. Bergmann, Leon E. Hirsch and Martin S. Klein, *The Impact of Highway Investment on Development*, The Brookings Institution, (Washington, D.C., 1966). Their approach is somewhat more general than that of the present study.

The Project

On May 29, 1959 the International Bank for Reconstruction and Development made a loan of US$72 million to the Government of Iran to assist in financing the road program in Iran's Second Seven-Year Development Plan (IRN–227). The Bank loan was to furnish the foreign exchange component estimated at US$69.6 million and local currency cost amounting to US$2.4 million. The total cost was estimated at US$185 million, including a 10 percent contingency allowance. Construction was expected to be completed by mid-1962. The project, subsequently somewhat reduced in scope, was actually completed in the fall of 1964; total expenditure was US$226 million.

Outline of Chapters

Chapter II gives the general transport setting and historical background of the project, with a review of some basic issues of economic priority. Chapter III inquires into the increases in costs and the delays in construction. Chapter IV considers typical construction costs by road type in Iran and the economic merits of stage construction; maintenance costs are placed in proper perspective. Chapter V and Annex I analyze the structure and growth of traffic. The chapter reviews traffic counts, vehicle registration and fuel consumption figures, origin and destination data from the registers of weighing stations, and import and railway statistics. It considers traffic diversion from the railways and discusses the future growth of traffic.

Chapter VI and Annex II analyze road user savings per vehicle resulting from the road improvements. Chapter VII deals with the development benefits that were expected to result. It asks whether lower transport costs have had any impact on agricultural output and comes to a negative conclusion.

Chapter VIII proffers a cost-benefit analysis of the various road sections in the project, the possible effect on the results of changes in the estimate of benefits, and the opportunities for alternative investment. Finally, Chapter IX draws general conclusions from the study and offers recommendations.

II

BACKGROUND AND HISTORY
OF THE PROJECT

The Pattern of Economic Activity

Iran is larger than Italy, Spain, France and Great Britain combined. About 90 percent of the land area consists of deserts and high mountains; inhabited areas are essentially "islands" scattered through the countryside. This combination of vast area and scattered population makes transportation costly.

Some 70 percent of the 21 million population reside in rural areas. Their main occupations are the production of staple crops (wheat, barley, rice, cotton) and livestock raising; agricultural yields are generally low. There is little industry aside from the processing of agricultural raw materials, but considerable mineral wealth; the mainstay of Iran's economy is petroleum, which at present contributes about half the government revenue each year, approximately $500 million.

The pattern of economic activity makes long distance transport important. Population and agricultural production are centered in the north, tapering off in a wide arc toward the south along the Iraq border. The sea ports are on the Persian Gulf in the southwest. Thus imports and exports require transport over long distances.

5

Also, both petroleum refining and crude oil production are concentrated in the southwest; the principal domestic consumption centers are in the north. In addition, there are many minerals produced in the north such as lead and chromite which require transport to the sea ports.

Modes of Transportation

Road and rail are the most important carriers, followed by pipelines for oil; air transport plays a supplementary role. In 1965 the road network consisted of about 32,000 kms: some 6,000 kms were asphalt, another 12,000 kms gravel, and the remaining 14,000 kms dirt roads and tracks. The railroad has about 3,500 kms of track. Intercity traffic on the three main carriers—road, rail and pipeline—was estimated at some 7.5 billion ton kms and some 4 billion passenger kms for 1959; roads may have accounted for some 60 percent of cargo and 50 percent of passenger traffic.

Most of Iran's foreign trade passes through the Gulf ports of Khoramshahr and Bandar Shahpoor. A new port is under construction at Bandar Abbas in the southeast. Upon completion, it is to take over part of the general cargo traffic of Khoramshahr to relieve the congestion there. The main rail line, the Trans-Iranian, connects the Gulf ports with Tehran and also with Bandar Shah on the Caspian Sea. Other lines extend from Tehran toward the northeast and the northwest; at Julfa, goods can be transshipped to the USSR network; still under construction is a 140 km extension from Tabriz to the Turkish rail system. Rail freight consists mainly of petroleum products, government imports of bulk commodities and general merchandise, mostly moving from south to north. Both rail freight and passenger traffic had been growing steadily, but in the past few years they have begun to decline somewhat. The railway, which is state-owned, has to cope with keen competition from road and pipeline transport.

The Roads Program in the First and Second Plans

At the end of World War II, the principal highways of Iran, generally following old caravan trails, ran from Khoramshahr to Tehran, from Baghdad to Tehran, from Tabriz via Tehran to

6

Mashhad, from Tehran through Qum to Esfahan, and from Kashan to Yazd. During the war there had been some repair and improvement of certain major roads by the Allied Powers, to facilitate the flow of military supplies to the Soviet Union, but few new roads were developed and, more significantly, regular road maintenance virtually stopped. As a result, Iran was left in the late 1940's with a highway network badly in need of major reconstruction. The Iranian Government decided to use a large part of its oil revenues for the economic development of the country. A "Plan Organization" was created independent of the existing ministries to prepare Iran's First Seven-Year Development Plan. A major item in the First Plan, which started in 1949, was the development of the country's system of communications. A list of roads was selected and a substantial sum of funds allocated.

The basis of this original list is unclear. No preliminary engineering was carried out to investigate construction problems and develop cost estimates. In any event, the government called in a foreign consulting firm, Overseas Consultants Inc. (OCI), to survey the country's roads, and particularly the list of road projects selected in the First Plan. With one minor addition, OCI concluded that the list included the major roads which they would recommend for development, amounting to 11,462 kms. OCI's report (1949) gave priority to roads connecting resources to centers of consumption, seaports to the interior, and major centers without alternative means of transport such as rail. One of OCI's recommendations is of direct relevance to this appraisal study. In view of the existing rail connection between Khoramshahr and Tehran, OCI recommended as the major north-south highway the Tehran-Esfahan-Shiraz-Bushire road. The alternative north-south route of the Trans-Iranian highway, which later became part of the loan project under study here, was not included.

Some of the road projects were started, but the political and economic crises of the early 1950's, following the nationalization of the oil industry, kept the Plan Program from being carried out. The First Plan came to a premature end in September 1955. The Second Seven-Year Plan, starting in 1955, provided for the improvement and reconstruction of 10,700 kms of road. The planning and supervision of some 6,000 kms of main road were to be undertaken by an international contracting firm under the general responsibility of the Plan Organization, and the balance of 4,700 kms by the Ministry of Roads.

It soon became evident that sufficient skilled manpower and equipment were not available for the execution of a program of this magnitude. Steadily increasing construction costs and more rigid specifications necessitated numerous revisions. The Second Plan program was drastically reduced; the Plan Organization cut the contract to 2,500 kms, while awarding another 1,100 kms to a Danish firm of consulting engineers, Kampsax.

Because of continued difficulties the original firm withdrew from the program in March 1958. The Plan Organization program was then further reduced from 3,600 kms to 2,470 kms and only the most important roads in Iran were included. The 1,370 kms not included in the Kampsax contract were divided in three sections and their design and execution assigned to three other consulting firms, 333 kms to an Iranian-French combination, Societe Etco, 419 kms to an Italian firm, Societa Sauti, and 614 kms to an American firm, Ammann & Whitney. Meanwhile the Ministry of Roads' share had fallen to 3,700 kms. Despite the drastic reduction in the whole program from 10,700 kms to 6,200 kms, the projected cost had now risen for the reasons stated above from an original Rials 10,593 million to Rials 11,850 million, and the cost per km nearly doubled to some Rials 1.9 million.

While the Plan Organization was responsible for the construction of that part of the road system which was to be financed by the oil revenues, the administration of the roads once built belongs to the Ministry of Roads. Table 1 shows that the total network maintained has expanded only slightly since 1957. The Iranian road program has largely comprised the upgrading of gravel roads to asphalt, which in 1966 covered some 6,000 kms against only 500 kms in 1957.

In the spring of 1957, the share of the Plan Organization of the oil revenue for the last four years of the Second Plan was cut from 80 to 60 percent.[1] This reduced the envisaged yield of oil revenues

---

[1] Actually, the proportion of oil revenue (net of the compensation of British Petroleum Company) going to the Plan Organization during the Second Plan never exceeded 55 percent.

TABLE 1:   Roads under Maintenance by the Ministry of Roads in Iran, 1957–1965

Year	Paved ('000 kms)	Paved (% of total)	Gravel ('000 kms)	Feeder or Earth ('000 kms)	Total ('000 kms)
1957	.5	1.7	16.1	13.4	30.0
1958	.7	2.3	15.9	13.6	30.2
1959	1.0	3.3	15.6	13.6	30.2
1960	1.3	4.3	15.5	13.7	30.5
1961	2.0	6.6	14.8	13.7	30.5
1962	2.5	8.1	14.3	13.9	30.7
1963	4.2	13.7	12.6	13.9	30.7
1964	4.8	15.5	12.0	14.2	31.0
1965[a]	5.1	16.5	11.7	14.2	31.0
1966[b]	6.0	19.2	11.0	14.2	31.2

[a] Provisional.
[b] Estimate.
Note: Excludes some forestry roads, and roads maintained by the Army, and by the National Iranian Oil Company, including some 850 kms of paved roads.
Source: Ministry of Roads, Tehran.

for the Plan from Rials 88 billion to Rials 76.5 billion, or by the equivalent of US$150 million, and raised the need for additional financing from abroad. Consequently the Government of Iran requested the World Bank in the spring of 1957 to participate in financing the revised road program. It is at this point that the project under review began to take shape.

The Project

A tentative revision of the road program was worked out through an exchange of views between the Bank and the Government of Iran beginning in the summer of 1957. The main element of this tentative program envisaged the construction and reconstruction of over 2,000 kms of main roads, including most of the 1,200 km Trans-Iranian highway. The rest were located mainly in the Kermanshah area. In the summer of 1958 the Bank assisted the government in preparing the project, including the working out of arrangements between the Plan Organization and the Ministry of Roads for the execution of the project. The original proposal was enlarged to include all of the Trans-Iranian highway, plus certain other important highway links. Furthermore, an agreement was reached to prepare a road program to be executed after completion of the project under negotiation. A detailed appraisal of the project was made by the Bank and, on May 29, 1959, the loan agreement was signed between the Government of Iran and the IBRD for US$72 million.

Description

As finally determined in the loan agreement, the "project" consisted of the following:

a) the construction and reconstruction of about 2,470 kms of main roads in western and southwestern Iran;

b) the improvement to year-round capability of the existing 440 km road between Khalafabad and Shiraz in the south;

c) the planning and preliminary engineering of a second main road program;

d) the planning and preliminary engineering of a feeder road program.

a) *The Main Road Program.* Very few of the roads in the main road program were new roads in the sense of opening virgin territory; they included nearly all the more important existing roads in their entire length (e.g. the Trans-Iranian Highway). Nevertheless, even the reconstruction of existing roads meant in many cases new embankments or new alignments. The project involved, therefore, the entire range from reconstruction, using the existing embankment, to relocation involving hundreds of kilometers of entirely new road.

TABLE 2: Main Road Program

Project road numbers		Planned	Built *(kms)*
I	Hamadan–Kermanshah–Shahabad–Khosravy	377	371
II	Shahabad–Malavi	157	158
III	Kermanshah–Divandareh–Saghez	325	306
IV	Bijar–Divandareh	70	55
V	Rudehen–Abegarm–Amol–Babol	175	156
VII	Ahwaz–Khalafabad–Sar Bandar	150	157
VI, XI, X, VIII and IX	Trans-Iranian Highway– Khoramshahr–Andimeshk–Malayer– Avadj–Ghazvin–Bandar Pahlavy	1,216	1,184
		2,470	2,387

The layout of the project is shown in Map 2. The Trans-Iranian highway, listed last in Table 2 above, was by far the longest road in the project, requiring substantial reconstruction as well as relocation; the road crosses a number of mountain ranges with passes at elevations between 1,000 and 1,600 meters. Road I extends westward from Hamadan on the Trans-Iranian through the regional center of Kermanshah to Khosravy on the Iraq border. These two main roads were to be connected with the region of Tabriz in the north via Roads II, III, and IV, located in hilly and mountainous country. Roads III and IV were to follow the general alignment of existing roads, but Road II, from Shahabad to Malavi in the west, would be entirely new construction. The remaining two roads in the main roads program are short but important links. North of Tehran, the Rudehen–Babol road, Road V, crosses the Elburz mountain range, parallel to the Caspian Sea, over a pass at 2,200 meters; traffic on the existing road had been interrupted for several years by severe washouts. The main road, VII, in the south, connects Ahwaz to Sar Bandar and the adjoining port of Bandar Shahpoor.

Execution

Construction and reconstruction of the projected 2,470 kms of main roads was executed under the responsibility of the Plan Organization; road surveys, design, and field supervision were carried out by the four consulting firms already at work in Iran: Kampsax (1,046 kms), Ammann & Whitney (585 kms), Sauti (440 kms), and Etco (316 kms). These firms were all experienced in this type of work.

The work program was divided into 43 contract sections and let on the basis of international competitive bidding. The great bulk of the work was obtained and carried out by local contractors. The main roads actually completed add up to only 2,387 kms, the difference from the projected 2,470 kms being due mainly to subsequent minor changes in alignment and greater precision in the measurement of distances. The workmanship was generally excellent, but construction costs were considerably higher than forecast. It was originally anticipated, in the appraisal report, that the work would be completed by mid-1962. The main part of the roads was

11

not completed until the end of 1963, and the remainder, comprising several short sections, was finished in 1964. The extension of the construction schedule has been ascribed to a combination of financial and technical difficulties. Most of the local contractors apparently underbid on the contracts and, in addition, were underfinanced. The contracts called for a sudden change over from hand labor to mechanical operation. Most of the local contractors did not possess the necessary equipment, finances and experience to make the switch smoothly. Also, local contractors were not accustomed to conform with set specifications; strict control of quality by the consultants undoubtedly contributed to slowing down the work schedule. The cost increases and construction delays are discussed in the next chapter.

b) *The Improvement in the South.* Connecting with Road VII at Khalafabad is a road of lower standards extending to Shiraz in an easterly direction. The existing connection was in poor condition; in fact, the 60 km section between Fahlian and Kazerun was only a trail and could not be used by normal trucks. The 440 km road was to be improved to make it passable all year round.

The work was executed by the Ministry of Roads' own forces under supervision of technical experts from the U.S. Bureau of Public Roads. Gaps in the existing road were closed by building some sections of low standard, and by bridging the rivers. The workmanship is good; the cost, $4 million.

c) *Planning a Second Program.* It was considered desirable to include the planning and preliminary engineering of a second main road program in the loan project. Although Iran was already devoting a substantial share of its investment resources to the current road construction program, further improvement of the road network was considered important and urgent. The Plan Organization and the Ministry of Roads, therefore, agreed in principle on the roads of highest priority for this next program. The foreign exchange component of consulting engineers' costs for surveys, studies and designs was included in the Bank loan. The execution of the second program was not to be started until the first had advanced to a stage where labor and equipment were freed for additional work.

The work proceeded smoothly. A reconnaissance survey was carried out for 6,475 kms of main roads, and a preliminary survey was made for 2,377 kms of the most important of these roads. These preparatory works served as a basis for a "Second Road Project" for which the Bank made a loan of $18.5 million in 1964. (See p. 16.)

d) *Feeder Roads*. Planning and preliminary engineering of feeder roads were also included in the project. Construction of extensive networks of "farm-to-market" roads was considered essential for raising agricultural production. Feeder roads had been neglected in the past, due to lack of funds and appropriate planning. Agreement on preparation of a feeder road program was reached among the relevant ministries, and the loan included an amount to cover the foreign exchange cost of consultant services.

Preparation of the feeder road program did not progress smoothly. There were protracted discussions on engineering procedures between the various government ministries and agencies concerned. It was 1963 before local consulting engineers were engaged for the reconnaissance and preliminary survey of about 7,000 kms of feeder roads in all 13 provinces of the country. Due to this late start, no disbursement was ever made out of the loan fund earmarked for feeder road engineering. Instead, the total amount was transferred to the fund for construction costs for the main highways.

Total Cost

The total cost of the whole project, a), b) and c), exceeded the original estimate by some 21 percent—over and above a contingency allowance of 10 percent included in the appraisal estimates. For the construction and reconstruction of the main roads alone, a), the cost increase over the original estimate (excluding the 10 percent contingency) was about 38 percent. It is with this section a) of the project that the Occasional Paper is henceforth concerned.

The Question of Priorities

Several important issues are raised by this brief survey of the background and history of the project. All through the development of the road program—the drawing up of the rather grandiose highway scheme of the First Plan, the choice of roads included in the Second Plan and the investigations leading to the "First Road Loan of 1959" (IRN–227)—there are unanswered questions as to the basis and justification of the selections made for the road improvements.[2] Numerous changes were made, and the scope of the program was severely curtailed, but the principles and facts underlying the determination of priorities in the successive stages are not clear. This priority question has many aspects. Complex problems are involved, and the authors have no illusions that they have come up with all the answers.

The most complicated sectoral issue in regard to this study concerns competition between rail and road. When the road program was initiated in the late 1940's, a rail connection already existed between the Gulf ports and Tehran, the major traffic artery of the country. In fact, as mentioned earlier, improvement of the Trans-Iranian highway was not included among the more than 11,000 kms of roads making up the program proposed by OCI. Yet, the Trans-Iranian highway figured prominently in the actual construction program. Could the railways, possibly only after improvements in operating efficiency and service, which themselves might have required additional investments, have handled the required transport volume through Khoramshahr more economically than trucks along the improved highway? Were there special reasons overriding the possible advantages of the railways and arguing in favor of improving the Trans-Iranian highway? To what extent does the existence of the rail alternative affect the benefits of reduced road user costs on the improved road? These are complicated questions which could only be partially answered within the resources of this study.

Within the roads program there were alternative possibilities for investment which were never systematically examined. For instance, there is little doubt that at least some feeder roads would have been of higher priority than some of the trunk roads that have been constructed or improved during the last decade. In some cases,

---

[2] The discussion here relates to the road program as a whole. A rather different question, not the concern of this study, relates to the considerations used by the Bank in selecting roads for financing from among those included in the road investment program finally arrived at.

lower-grade trunk roads combined with more feeder roads were likely to have been economically preferable to the more expensive of the main roads included in the program. Due to the content of the project, however, problems of feeder roads were outside the terms of reference of this study.

The priority of feeder roads was but a special case of priorities within the program. Again, on what basis were some roads excluded when the program had to be curtailed, and even more, what were the reasons, in those circumstances, for substituting other roads while many of those on the original list had to be postponed? There may have been good reasons, economic or otherwise, for these changes, but the economic priority of some of the roads included is not immediately obvious and it is not clear that a thorough investigation was made of the relative economic merits of the various roads, taking into account their current state, cost of improvement, current and expected traffic, etc. The absence of the necessary information merely pushes the question of priorities one step further back: priority should have been given to the systematic collection of relevant data.

Furthermore, the authors doubt whether the priority for improving a particular highway or road is the most meaningful question. The need for improvement is almost bound to vary between the various segments of a road. In the extreme case of the Trans-Iranian highway, for example, the road is some 1,200 kms long. Analysis of priority is scarcely relevant in such a case unless it differentiates between smaller road segments for which present and future traffic, the state of the road, cost of improvements, etc. are likely to vary widely. Improvement of some segments may indeed be of high priority, while that of others may be a misuse of scarce resources.

A later Bank-financed road investment in Iran, which might or might not have been foreseen in 1958, spotlights this issue clearly. Under the terms of the Bank's Second Road Project of 1964, the road Burujird–Qum–Tehran, following roughly the alignment of the railway and of the traditional main trade route of Iran, is being completed to main road standards. It cuts 180 kms off the distance from the Gulf ports to Tehran via Ghazvin. For this reason its justification in terms of economic net benefits is quite certain; indeed this Paper will suggest (Annex I, p. 107) that 95 percent of the northbound traffic between Hamadan and Ghazvin is bound for Tehran and will find the new route shorter. Thus the new project will switch traffic away from the Burujird–Ghazvin sections of the Trans-Iranian highway, Roads VIII and X of this project (and part of XI), and probably take away the economic justification for the capital expenditure on their improvement. Plainly the principle which emerges from this history is that all possible developments and alternatives should be assessed before embarking on a transport program.

In a given program, the real choice may not always be between improving either one road segment or another. The best solution may be to provide limited improvements for both segments. Overcoming serious bottlenecks such as narrow bridges, or improving only the worst stretches of road—curves, grades and surface—may make the greatest contribution to reducing transport costs possible with the available resources. While fractional analysis of roads is now accepted practice for road project analysis,[3] it was not always used in the past in drawing up road programs, as witness this example.

The economizing of investment resources, for instance, is clearly related to design standards and types of pavement for various classes of roads. For a given amount of investment resources, you can have fewer but better roads or more but poorer roads. Whether such decisions can be made sensibly depends on the quality of the available data, construction and maintenance costs, road user costs, traffic volumes. Construction of some roads by stages is another possibility that ought to have been considered. Its disadvantage is that absolute costs are greater; its advantage that the successive upgrading of the road can be phased more closely to the growth in traffic. A further problem of particular interest in Iran concerns the permissible maximum axle weights—overloading used to be common and its effects on roads disastrous. It is difficult to assess the additional costs and benefits of building roads to withstand axle-loads greater than those common in most other countries.

---

[3] See Hans A. Adler, *Sector and Project Planning in Transportation*, World Bank Staff Occasional Paper No. 4, (1967).

In sum, the economic aspects appear to have received insufficient attention from the start. The development of the road project under study and the initial appraisal are bound to have suffered to some extent from these background weaknesses. Nor could a reappraisal effort fully investigate all the economic questions raised by the issue of priorities. In hindsight, a traffic survey, for instance, would have increased the validity of the conclusions reached. But the authors believe that the study has identified factors which are of crucial importance for the analysis of road projects. Not the least of these factors, as it turns out, is the rigorous analysis of economic questions.

III

ANALYSIS OF CONSTRUCTION COSTS
AND SCHEDULES

Original Estimates and Actual Costs

The authors' analysis is confined to the 2,470 kms of main roads—
the principal part of the project. The Bank's appraisal report, made
at the time the loan agreement was signed in May, 1959, estimated
the total cost of (re)constructing the main roads at Rials 11,785
million (US$157.1 million). This estimate excluded the contingency
allowance of 10 percent, but included all construction and consultants' costs incurred as from April 21, 1958. The construction
contracts between the Plan Organization and the contractors were
so-called "unit price contracts." These contracts carried detailed
specifications of the work to be done at a stated price, e.g. X cubic
meters of earth excavation at Y rials per cubic meter; an average
contract contained about 100 such specifications. The contracts did
not provide for "escalation" whereby the contractor is entitled to
pass on to the principal certain price increases, such as in wage rates
or material prices. All contracts set a definite time limit for completion of construction, with penalties for delays.

In view of these factors—detailed engineering surveys already
made, most of the contracts signed, and lack of escalation clauses—

it was expected in 1959 that the final cost estimate would come quite close to the original. The Bank's project appraisal report stated: "the [*cost*] estimates are relatively reliable as detailed engineering plans have in all cases been prepared and contracts have been awarded covering the major part of the roads included in the program. The accuracy of the estimate is therefore mainly subject to variations in the quantities and possible extra work. For these reasons an additional 10 percent [*included*] for unforeseen expenses can be considered sufficient." [1] However, the final costs of US$210 million exceeded the Bank's original estimate by about 34 percent; the average cost per road km increased from about Rials 4.9 million to Rials 6.6 million, or from US$65,800 to US$88,000.

For purposes of cost analysis, the project is divided into 11 roads (see Map 2). The Bank's data were not detailed enough for road-by-road analysis, so the authors secured cost data—estimates and actual costs—by submitting questionnaires to the four consulting firms charged with supervising the road program. Total actual costs according to the consultants were $216.5 million, or $6.5 million above the Bank's final figure. The authors, after studying the differences, concluded that reconciliation was not worth the considerable time required. The extra $6.5 million may broadly have corresponded with work on the project roads which was strictly outside the Bank's terms of reference—specifically the resurfacing of the Hamadan–Malayer road, the relocation of the National Iranian Oil Company's pipeline, and Kampsax' consultancy fees before August 1959. These would represent an addition of 4 percent to the contract value of the project, or 10 percent of the overrun. In an economic sense these charges are properly attributed to the project, however, and in this study the consultants' figures are used throughout.

Reasons for Cost Increases Given in Progress Reports

Successive progress reports tell a story of cumulative difficulties. Excerpts from these reports are given below in chronological order.

"Some [*contractors*] are already having difficulties due to miscalculation of prices and the fact that contracts were awarded to them at too low prices and contrary to the awarding recommendations

---

[1] The quotation is from an internal Bank report which is not available for public distribution. Further references to Bank internal documents will not be footnoted.

TABLE 3: Actual Construction and Consultants' Costs of Main Roads in the Project

	Road	Length (kms)	Actual Cost[a] total (million rials)	per kilometer (million rials)
I	Hamadan–Khosravy	371	1,888	5.1
II	Shahabad–Malavi	158	905	5.7
III	Kermanshah–Saghez	306	1,154	3.8
IV	Divandareh–Bijar	55	135	2.5
V	Rudehen–Babol	156	2,203	14.1
VI	Khoramshah–Andimeshk	283	1,872	6.6
VII	Ahwaz–Sar Bandar	157	888	5.7
VIII	Avadj–Ghazvin	112	581	5.2
IX	Ghazvin–Bandar Pahlavy	204	2,546	12.5
X	Avadj–Malayer	202	1,051	5.2
XI	Malayer–Andimeshk	383	3,016	7.9
	Total actual costs I–XI	2,387	16,240	6.8
	US dollars		216.5 mn.	90,700

[a] The "actual cost" data by roads include both construction (contractors' costs) and consultants' costs. Because consultants costs are not available by individual road, only by consultant, their costs have been apportioned to the different roads in proportion with the construction costs incurred for each road.

Sources: Data obtained from the four consulting firms, Kampsax, Sauti, ETCO, and Ammann & Whitney in Tehran, spring 1965.

of Kampsax. The problem was recently discussed between Kampsax and the Plan Organization. A cancellation of the contracts would mean delay and higher costs. It was therefore decided to seek ways and means to help the contractors financially by allowing payment for additional work in cases where such payments could to a great extent be justified." (October 5, 1959.)

"The low prices originally offered by the contractors and the lack of proper organization and operation in the field, despite the consultants' effort to provide technical assistance, has compelled the Plan Organization to assist the contractors financially within the framework of their contract to see the work through." (October 28, 1960.)

"Due to the heavy financial burden put on each of the contractors for procuring the necessary equipment, most of the contractors have had great difficulty in obtaining sufficient local funds needed as working capital. The contractors have at times been compelled to seek short-term loans in the Tehran Bazaar at prohibitive interest (today 20–30%)." (October 28, 1960.)

21

"The increase [*in construction costs*] reflects a more exact calculation of costs by the four consultants as the work proceeds and also reflects the extra costs of contracts being withdrawn because the contractor was not able to continue and had to be replaced." (October 16, 1961.)

"The engineering fees have also increased . . . reflecting the lengthened construction time of most of the sections running closely to September 1962." (October 16, 1961.)

"Considering all the difficulties encountered with inexperienced contractors, the awards of contracts at unrealistically low prices, and a 30 percent increase in cost of living since the work started, the increase in total cost is tolerable." (October 11, 1962.)

"The increase [*in costs over the original estimate*] must be regarded as moderate considering the difficulties encountered with inexperienced local contractors, who had to switch from hand labor to fully mechanized operation. The extra cost paid may be regarded as a contribution toward the training of contractors in modern construction methods." (October 4, 1963.)

Analysis of Reasons for Cost Increases

The costs of *construction* of each road section (excluding consultants' charges) are summarized in Table 4. The table shows the consultants' estimate prior to bidding, the contract price after bidding and the actual costs of construction. The final total is 40 percent above the contract price. The contract prices however were on average 7 percent below the consultants' estimates. Or to put it another way, if the overrun is taken as 100 percent, the difference between "the too low initial bids" of contractors (frequently mentioned in the progress reports) and the consultants' estimates, accounted for only 15 percent. Extra-contract work may have accounted for a further 10 percent, and another 75 percent remains to be accounted for.

Further information on possible causes of the increase in costs was obtained from a questionnaire. Because the information obtained for some lots was insufficient, the analysis here is based on a sample comprising all lots with adequate information. The sample is both large and representative, covering approximately 75 percent

TABLE 4: Construction Costs, by Road, according to the Consultants

Road	Consultants' estimate	Contract price	Actual costs	Consultants' estimate	Actual costs
		(million rials)		(contract price = 100)	
I Hamadan–Khosravy	1,246	1,124	1,653	111	147
II Shahabad–Malavi	533	478	792	112	166
III Kermanshah–Saghez	875	864	1,010	101	117
IV Divandareh–Bijar	100	100	118	100	118
V Rudehen–Babol	1,207	1,163	1,928	104	166
VI Khoramshahr–Andimeshk	..	(1,499)	(1,634)	..	(109)
VII Ahwaz–Sar Bandar	721	698	775	103	111
VIII Avadj–Ghazvin	360	333	550	108	165
IX Ghazvin–Bandar Pahlavy	1,715	1,567	2,407	109	154
X Avadj–Malayer	754	716	966	105	135
XI Malayer–Andimeshk	2,008	1,855	2,773	108	150
Total	9,519	8,897	12,972	107	146
Total, incl. VI	..	(10,397)	(14,606)	..	(140)

Note: Data on road VI are incomplete; this explains the cost increase of 46 percent (last column) as compared with 40 percent when Road VI is included.
Source: The consultants, Tehran, 1965.

in terms both of contract prices and actual costs. The reasons cited for the cost increase and their relative importance are as follows:

Reasons Cited	Accounting for Construction Cost Increase of	
	(million rials)	(percent)
Additional work and changes in design	1,312.8	44
Increase in quantities due to underestimation of the work	1,199.3	39
Increase above the contract unit prices (e.g., price per cubic meter of excavation)	301.7	10
"Force majeure" (floods, landslides, etc.)	160.5	5
Miscellaneous (special payments, Plan Organization)	72.7	2
Total cost increase	3,047.1	100

The unit prices referred to in the contracts were not subject to change, in the absence of an escalation clause. But in any case the general price increase in Iran during the construction period was fairly limited:

	1959	1960	1961	1962	1963[a]
Wholesale price index	100	102	104	104	104
Cost of living index	100	110	115	115	116

[a] There was a 4 percent increase in prices in 1964 and a 2 percent increase in 1965, but these should not have affected construction costs contracted before those years.
Source: IMF *International Financial Statistics.*

23

The two most important factors which are said to have caused costs to increase, together accounting for over 80 percent of the total, are "additional work and changes in design" and "increase in quantities due to underestimation of the work."

There is no doubt that original underestimation of quantities by the consultants occurred. The variations in cost appear to have come mainly from variations in the composition of the material to be excavated, the percentage of rock in relation to earth. This is one of the most difficult tasks for the consultants to estimate in advance.

Table 5 analyzes the cost increases by category of lot. The classification is somewhat rough, but nevertheless it would seem pertinent that costs have risen most for lots in difficult terrain where such a problem is most likely to be encountered. Increases are least in flat or rolling terrain (24 percent), becoming progressively larger in mountainous/flat (37 percent) and mountainous terrain (60 percent). Cost overruns in lots in mountainous area—i.e. 29 percent of all lots by contract value—accounted in fact for nearly half the total increase in costs.

TABLE 5: Construction Cost Increases, by Category of Lot

Category	Contract Prices (million rials)	(percent)	Actual Costs (contract prices of each category = 100)	Cost Increase (contract prices of all lots = 100)
Cancelled contracts[a]	1,337	12.3	170	9
Bridge lots	380	3.7	107	—
Lots in mountainous terrain	2,996	29.0	160	18
Lots in mountainous/flat terrain	724	7.0	137	2
Lots in flat or rolling terrain	4,961	48.0	124	12
All lots	10,397	100	140	40

[a] Construction completed, but by different contractors.
Source: The consultants, Tehran, 1965.

Inability of the contractor to finish the job affected about 12 percent of all lots in terms of contract prices, but accounted for nearly a quarter of the total increase in construction costs. Where a contract for a lot was cancelled, the average increase in costs for the lot was as high as 70 percent. The progress report of October 1961 gave withdrawal from contracts as one of the reasons for escalating costs. According to the *Tehran Journal* of April 6, 1965: "The Government is planning to compile a list (*black list*) of defaulting contractors and bar them from taking part in bidding for state contracts." Moreover, a second list would be made comprising contractors approved on the basis of a judgment as to their "competence . . . governed by their financial and technical capability and experience." And their financial difficulties were to be eased since, "in the case of construction . . . once a tender or bid is declared awarded, the government department concerned is authorized to pay an advance up to 25 percent of the work involved to the winning contractor."

Because of the inexperience of local contractors and the low bid prices they quoted, the Plan Organization was compelled to choose between two alternatives: the first was to cancel contracts and ask for new bids for the unfinished part of the works, which meant delays in execution and higher unit prices by the new contractor; the second was to help the contractor financially within the legal framework of his contract. A road contract is never a perfect legal document, with no loopholes or problems of interpretation. The contractors' difficulties probably resulted in a "liberal" interpretation of their claims.

A straightforward conclusion from the evidence is that the major reason for the cost overrun of 40 percent—four times the normal 10 percent contingency allowance—was that the preparation did not take sufficient account of all the factors. Among these were certainly the serious difficulties that the contractors were likely to face. Increases in unit prices and "force majeure" played only minor roles, as did extra work outside the project as defined by the Bank.

The foregoing discussion has focused on the increases in construction costs. Increases in consultants' costs have, on the average, been of the same order. However, this does not hold true for each of the consultants separately.

A detailed analysis of the reasons underlying these increases has not been undertaken; their impact on total costs is small anyway. Most of the increase in consultants' costs—mainly for supervision—is probably related to construction delays, which are discussed in the following section.

TABLE 6:   Analysis of Consultants' Costs

Consultants	Actual construction costs	Actual consultants' costs	Total costs	Consultants' costs as percent of construction costs	
	(original contracts = 100)			Original	Actual
Kampsax	148	130	145	16.2	14.3
SAUTI	110	147	113	10.9	14.6
ETCO	156	111	152	8.1	5.8
Ammann & Whitney	145	159	146	8.1	8.8
Total	140	136	140	11.6	11.2

Source: The consultants, Tehran, 1965.

Delays in Construction

All construction contracts contained a definite time limit within which the work had to be finished. However, in most cases the contractor needed more time. Although the contracts contained a provision for penalties for delays which could be attributed to the contractor, in practice this provision was not enforced. Information on these delays was collected from the consultants. For purposes of analysis, the total number of lots has been broken down into the same categories as before. Some 5 percent of all lots had to be left out because of insufficient information, and the categories "mountainous/flat" and "flat or rolling" have been combined into "remaining lots." The relative importance of each category, in terms of actual costs, is as follows:

Category	Actual Cost	
	(million rials)	*(percent)*
Cancelled contracts	2,266.1	16.4
Bridge lots	238.1	1.7
Mountainous lots	4,726.9	34.2
Remaining lots	6,579.9	47.7
Total lots	13,811.0	100.0
All lots	14,605.8	

The progress of construction by category of lot is presented graphically in Chart I. The analytical procedure was, for each lot, to construct an ideal original schedule in which an equal percentage

26

of work by value was allotted to each quarter up to the completion date in the contract. From this an ideal time schedule for each category, shown under broken lines in Chart 1, was constructed by weighting each lot with its actual construction cost. The actual time schedules, similarly combined by category, are drawn alongside (unbroken lines). Both schedules add to 100%. It will be seen that the bridge lots experienced hardly any delay—the sample is admittedly rather small, comprising only 60 percent of all bridge lots. By contrast, work which experienced cancelled contracts and work on mountainous terrain was seriously delayed.

The problem then was to express the average delay by category in months. A rather crude measure may be obtained by comparing completion dates. This is done below by category, with each lot again weighted according to its actual costs. On this basis, work affected by cancelled contracts and on mountainous lots was delayed by some two years, and that on lots in easier terrain by one year.

Category	Delay in Months
Cancelled contracts	24.4
Bridge lots	1.5
Mountainous lots	26.5
Remaining lots	12.5
Total lots	19.1

Delay however comprises two components: the length of the delay, and the proportion of work by value included in the delay. This has been taken into account in Table 8 which shows the average delay per lot in months, with delays weighted by corresponding values of work.[2] These average delays have been combined by category of lot, weighted again by actual construction costs. The

[2] The method of computation may be clarified by the following simplified example, where total actual costs of a lot are 80 monetary units—

Month (t)	1	2	3	4	5	6 -----n
Original schedule (a_t)	20	20	20	20	—	— -----a_n
Actual schedule (b_t)		10	20	20	20	10 -----b_n

Average delay (D) in months is obtained by:

$$D = \frac{\sum_{t=1}^{t=n} t(b_t - a_t)}{\sum_{t=1}^{t=n} a_t} = \frac{-20 - 20 + 0 + 0 + 100 + 60}{80} = \frac{120}{80} = 1\frac{1}{2} \text{ months}$$

CHART I

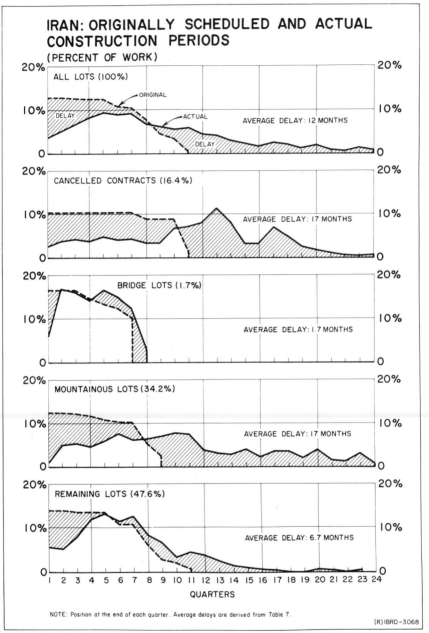

IRAN: ORIGINALLY SCHEDULED AND ACTUAL CONSTRUCTION PERIODS
(PERCENT OF WORK)

ALL LOTS (100%)

ORIGINAL

DELAY

ACTUAL

AVERAGE DELAY: 12 MONTHS

DELAY

CANCELLED CONTRACTS (16.4%)

AVERAGE DELAY: 17 MONTHS

BRIDGE LOTS (1.7%)

AVERAGE DELAY: 1.7 MONTHS

MOUNTAINOUS LOTS (34.2%)

AVERAGE DELAY: 17 MONTHS

REMAINING LOTS (47.6%)

AVERAGE DELAY: 6.7 MONTHS

1 2 3 4 5 6 7 8 9 10 11 12 13 14 15 16 17 18 19 20 21 22 23 24

QUARTERS

NOTE: Position at the end of each quarter. Average delays are derived from Table 7.

(R) IBRD-3068

results in Table 7 indicate, of course, delays smaller than those of the analysis in the preceding paragraph which are heavily influenced by the tail end of construction which involved very little remaining work. For all lots together, the delay is reduced from 19 to 12 months. The structure of delays by category of lot remains the same: it is greatest for "cancelled contracts" and "mountainous lots." The results for cost increases and for delays are strikingly similar:

TABLE 7:   Comparison of Construction Delays and Cost Increases by Category of Lot

Category	Average Delay		Cost Increase	
	(*months*)	(*all lots* = *100*)	(*percent*)	(*all lots* = *100*)
Cancelled contracts	17	142	70	171
Bridge lots	1.7	14	7	17
Mountainous lots	17	142	60	146
Remaining lots	6.7	56	26	63
Total lots	12	100	40	100

Reasons Given by the Consultants

The opinion of the four consultants themselves was then sought directly. Given the more or less objectively known total delay for each individual lot, they were asked by questionnaire to estimate the contribution, in terms of months, of each of several possible reasons for delay. The results, summarized in Table 8, are again weighted by the actual costs of each lot and distinguish between mountainous and the remaining lots. The replies put greater emphasis on the lack of experience of contractors and on changes in design etc., and less emphasis on underestimation in the original contract.

One important aspect is that for the first time in Iran's history, road contracts were awarded for execution by mechanized operation. Iranian road contractors had had very little experience with such methods, and neither the contractors nor the consultants were able to establish the exact time needed for the execution of such work because they had no past experience in Iran on which to base such a judgment. The construction periods stipulated by the consultants in the different contracts were based on their experience in other countries. It turned out, however, that the contractor's actual

TABLE 8: Reason for Delay in Work

Main Responsible Party	Total lots	Mountainous lots	Remaining lots
	(total months of delay = 100)		
I. Contractors			
(a) lack of experience	19.5	19.3	19.8
(b) financing difficulties	9.1	13.3	2.6
(c) equipment problems	9.3	11.4	6.3
Sub-total	37.9	44.0	28.7
II. Consultants			
(d) underestimation in original contract	13.4	11.0	17.1
(e) changes in design of the road and additional work	19.1	17.2	22.0
Sub-total	32.5	28.2	39.1
III. Government			
(f) difficulties in relation to pipeline (NIOC)	5.7	9.4	—
(g) delay in award of hot mix addition	2.7	—	6.7
(h) delay in payment by Plan Organization	3.3	1.7	5.8
(i) delay in expropriation of right-of-way	2.2	3.7	—
Sub-total	13.9	14.8	12.5
IV. "Force Majeure"			
(j) delay in supply of detonators	1.6	2.7	—
(k) unforeseen difficulties, long winters, heavy rains	13.4	10.3	17.9
(l) labor problems	0.7	—	1.8
Sub-total	15.7	13.0	19.7
Total	100.0	100.0	100.0
In months	18.4	26.5	12.5
Total actual costs *(million rials)*	10,306.2	4,726.9	6,579.3

Note: "Cancelled contracts" and "bridge lots" (cf. Table 7) are excluded because of lack of information. Total delay in months refers here to simple delays *not* weighted by the amounts of work affected.
Source: The consultants, Tehran, 1965.

performance was lower than expected, he needed more time to learn the new methods than originally anticipated.

From the first road project, both consultants and contractors have learned their lessons. For the second road project, the contractual construction schedule for the individual sections was set more realistically and in general is observed by the contractors. On some sections work has been completed 4–5 months ahead of time.

IV

ADDITIONAL COST INFORMATION

Typical Construction Costs

There is a dearth of practical comparative information on costs of road-building and road maintenance in developing countries. This chapter summarizes the answers to questions that are often asked in economic analysis: specifically (a) what are typical costs of constructing different qualities of road, and (b) what is the impact on cost of constructing a road in several stages instead of all at once?

Two of the consulting firms (Kampsax and Ammann & Whitney) prepared detailed estimates of "typical" costs of road construction in Iran. The estimates differentiate:

a. The type of surface (asphalt, gravel or earth).
b. The width of the road (7 or 6 meters).
c. The maximum axle load the road should be able to withstand (14 or 8 tons).
d. The type of terrain—"mountainous," "flat or rolling" (Kampsax) or "normal" (Ammann & Whitney).

The estimates are given in detail in Tables 12, 13, and 14 and summarized in Table 9 below. They are based partly on the actual experience of the consultants in Iran and partly on engineering relationships. Most relevant for the purpose of this section are the relative, rather than the absolute, costs of the different types of road. Relative costs are found by using index numbers, taking as 100 the construction (contractors') costs per km of a 7-meter wide asphalt road for axle loads of up to 14 tons. Most of the consultants' experience was with this type of road.[1]

TABLE 9: Typical Construction Cost per km in Iran, 1965
(cost of 7 meter paved road, with 14 ton axle-load limit = 100)

Road Type	Paved		Gravel		Earth	
width, meters	7	6	7	6	7	6
For axle-load limit of 14 tons						
Mountainous[a]	100	90	94	85	..	..
Normal[b]	100	90	71	65	43	39
Flat or rolling[c]	100	88	80	69	..	..
For axle-load limit of 8 tons						
Mountainous	98	89	92	84	..	..
Normal	86	78	71	65	43	39
Flat or rolling	91	81	70	62	..	..

[a] Rials 18.4 million per km = 100.
[b] Rials 5.9 million per km = 100.
[c] Rials 5 million per km = 100.
Sources: For road construction costs in "mountainous" and "flat or rolling" terrain, Kampsax. For "normal" terrain, Ammann & Whitney. See Tables 12, 13 and 14 for more details.

Cost estimates for roads through "normal" terrain were computed by Ammann & Whitney; and for those through "flat or rolling" terrain by Kampsax, independently of each other. These estimates, for more or less similar conditions, are sufficiently close to inspire confidence in the general validity of all the estimates.

However, the estimates are for "typical" roads only. The ratio of construction cost estimates for "typical" roads in mountainous terrain to those for flat or rolling terrain is $3\frac{1}{2}$:1 (Kampsax). Yet for the entire project the ratio of *actual* construction costs of mountainous to the remaining roads was only 2:1. This was because the

---

[1] Asphalt roads in Iran are of the heavy 4 to 6 cm "hot carpet" type. Experience with lighter types had proved unsatisfactory.

project roads through "flat or rolling" and "flat/mountainous" terrain were more varied than those labeled "typical" in the consultants' estimates. The high cost estimate for mountainous roads also reflects Kampsax' experience with the Rudehen–Babol road, crossing the Elburz range.

These estimates are of roads "typical" of Iran only. Yet, on account of their great detail they may serve as useful indicators of *relative* costs of road-building in different terrain in other countries.

The data broadly suggest the following conclusions: for flat or rolling terrain, the type of surface is the most important cost factor. Substituting gravel for asphalt (or earth for gravel) reduces costs by about 20–25 percent; but making the road 6 rather than 7 meters, or reducing its strength from a maximum axle weight of 14 to 8 tons, cuts costs by only half that percentage, say 10–12 percent. In mountainous terrain, however, width is the most important factor. A reduction of 1 meter in width cuts costs by 10 percent compared with 6 percent for a substitution of gravel for asphalt. Axle loads, in this case, play a minor role: an axle-load weight limit of 8 instead of 14 tons reduces construction costs by only about 2 percent. It will be seen from the comparisons above that the percentage savings possible are smaller in mountainous terrain. However, as overall construction costs in mountains are higher, *absolute* cost savings from substituting an inferior surface or lowering the axle-load limit are about the same in both types of terrain, as might be expected.

Which of the cost components, in the opinion of the consultants, are mainly affected by changes in standards? By comparison with asphalt roads, gravel roads eliminate pavement costs and increase costs of the base (according to Kampsax) or greatly reduce costs of the base or sub-base (according to Ammann & Whitney). A narrower road tends to reduce all cost items.

On paved roads lower maximum axle-load limit permits, in most cases, elimination of the cost of the sub-base and reduction in the cost of the base. These results depend to some extent on how costs are broken down between base and sub-base. However, according to Ammann & Whitney a lower axle-load limit does not significantly reduce construction costs of gravel and earth roads.

Consultants' costs amount to 16 percent and vary with the cost of the road (Kampsax), or start at 10 percent and rise to about 13 percent on lower-grade roads (Ammann & Whitney). These percentages are roughly in line with actual consultants' costs on the project.

An important tentative conclusion can be drawn at this point. In flat or rolling terrain, constructing a gravel road instead of an asphalt road and reducing its width by one meter may mean a cost reduction of 30–35 percent; or, in other words, the paved, one-meter wider road is about 50 percent more expensive. This is a significant difference suggesting that, for low traffic volumes, lower standard roads may offer an economic alternative. If user savings are the principal benefit, the data also suggest that road user savings per km on a mountain road must be two to four times as high as on a road through flat or rolling terrain to yield the same rate of return. Alternatively, the required traffic volume should be correspondingly larger.

Stage Construction

Road construction is often possible in stages, i.e. the road is improved in successive steps, instead of all at once. In this way, road standards can be more closely geared to the development of traffic. The raising of standards in stages is technically less efficient, however, and thus raises the overall (*undiscounted*) construction costs. The economic issue is whether the advantages of postponing part of the investment outlays outweigh the disadvantages of higher overall costs and initially lower benefits.

It is often said that stage construction may in theory be interesting but in practice very seldom is worth considering because of the prohibitive increase in total (*undiscounted*) costs as compared with single-stage construction. Some relevant data are shown in Table 10 which compares the cost of single-stage construction of a paved road 6 or 7 meters wide with the cost of first building a gravel road of 5 or 6 meters respectively, and only subsequently paving and widening it.

The data indicate that the additional costs involved in stage construction may be only some 5 percent. According however to another expert opinion, based on the same example, the additional costs of stage construction may be some 10–15 percent.[2] Whatever the precise magnitude, these figures indicate that the extra cost for stage construction is not *a priori* prohibitive.[3]

TABLE 10:   Cost of Paving a Road by Stages

(million rials per km)

Costs	Two-Stage Construction (1)	Single-Stage Construction (2)	Difference in Costs (1) − (2)
Gravel, 5 m wide	2.77		
Paving and widening to 6 m	2.0		
Paved road, 6 m wide	4.77	4.50	.27
Gravel, 6 m wide	3.46		
Paving and widening to 7 m	2.60		
Paved road, 7 m wide	6.06	5.77	.29

Note: The data refer to average conditions. Though not fully comparable to "normal" or "flat or rolling" conditions in Table 9, costs per km are roughly in line.
Source: Kampsax, *Second Road Program,* Phase I, Vol. I, p. 43 and Appendix 118, 1960.

Stage construction deserves a good deal more attention as an economic alternative than it is often given in road planning. In the second example above, undertaking only the first stage reduces costs by 5.77 − 3.46 = 2.31 million rials. At a discount rate of 10 percent, a one year postponement of the second stage thus implies a cost saving of .23 million rials. On the other hand, the extra cost of construction in stages amounts to .29 million rials. Consequently, unless benefits are significantly reduced by postponement, even a deferment of a little more than one year would offset the additional cost of stage construction. In the first example above, a deferment of under two years would similarly offset the additional cost.[4]

---

[2] Because there would be a higher cost per cubic meter for widening the road than for its original construction.

[3] For similar example, see R. Winfrey, *Cost Comparison of Four-Lane Stage Construction on Interstate Highways,* Highway Research Board Bulletin 306, (Washington, D.C., 1961).

[4] In addition there are often real advantages to postponement apart from capital saving: if the benefits are uncertain, the greater knowledge to be gained in a year's delay may be worth a price. See A. A. Walters, *The Economics of Road User Charges,* Occasional Paper No. 5, Chapter III.

Road Maintenance

Maintenance is important in preserving the investment made in roads. It is relatively unimportant, however, as a cost item. Annual maintenance costs, according to Ammann & Whitney, amount roughly to only 1 percent of construction costs for asphalt and earth roads and somewhat less for gravel (consultants' costs are excluded). More concisely, total maintenance costs, over a twenty-five-year life of the road and at a discount rate of 10 percent, are in present value only some 9 percent of construction costs, and even less at higher rates of interest or over a shorter life of the road. Moreover, this refers to gross maintenance costs, not to the difference between maintenance costs on the old road and those on the new one.

More detailed information on maintenance costs by type of road was obtained from three different sources: Ammann & Whitney, advisers from the U.S. Bureau of Public Roads working in Tehran, and the Ministry of Roads, Iran.

TABLE 11: Annual Maintenance Cost by Type of Road,
Data from Three Sources

('000 rials per km)

Type of Road	Ammann & Whitney	Bureau of Public Roads	Ministry of Roads	Used for Cost-benefit analysis, Chapter VIII
High quality paved	60	63	50	60
Low quality paved		70		
Gravel	30–34	67	32–50	35
Earth	23–26	28		25

Except for the estimate for maintenance of gravel roads, the Bureau of Public Roads estimates are fairly consistent; however, they were probably not wholly independently obtained. In Iran, maintenance costs per km appear to rise with the standard of the road, not so much because of purely routine maintenance (clearing of ditches, etc.) but because of the costs of resurfacing every four to five years. The costs quoted apply to the range of traffic normal for each category of road, higher for paved roads, lower for earth roads. Since total maintenance costs rise with the level of traffic, maintenance costs for the same volume of traffic differ less between different types of road. The authors were unable, however, to secure any statistical data on the relation between the volume of traffic and corresponding maintenance costs in Iran.[5] The authors also tried to obtain information on maintenance costs in physical terms for different types of road, e.g. the size and composition of a maintenance crew, with specified equipment necessary for maintaining a certain length and type of road on a year-round basis. But such data did not seem to be available.

Maintenance of the roads included in the project appears to be adequate. They were generally in good condition during the authors' visit in the spring of 1965. This is not a very rigorous test, however, as they had only recently been completed. Maintenance activity was in evidence: on several occasions small maintenance crews of two to four men were observed clearing the roads of fallen rocks and cleaning out drainage ditches. In financial terms, total annual maintenance expenditure amounts currently to around Rials 30,000 per km for some 31,000 kms of road. (See Table 1, p. 9.) Given a road network consisting of asphalt, gravel and earth roads roughly in the proportion 1:2:2.5, recent maintenance expenditure has been somewhat lower than the maintenance costs shown in Table 11. A sharp increase was, however, expected for 1965.[6]

---

[5] International literature provides some estimates of the relationship between volume of traffic and road maintenance costs; e.g. R. S. Millard, *Roads, Road Transport, and Traffic in Developing Countries*, Conference on Civil Engineering, (London, 1962), suggests "that the expression $50 + 2Q$ can be used to give an approximate indication of the cost of maintaining an improved, gravel surface road in pounds per mile per year," where Q stands for the average daily traffic flow in vehicles. Similar formulas are also presented by the U.N. Economic Commission for Africa, *African Transport Development Study*, Part I, (E/CN 14/Trans/28, 1965, p. 102). There is some evidence that with rising volumes of traffic maintenance costs rise faster on low quality roads than on higher quality roads. R. M. Soberman, *Economic Analyses of Highway Design in Developing Countries*, Highway Research Record No. 115, Highway Research Board, (Washington, D.C., 1966) gives the following formulas derived from Venezuelan data, in Bolivars per km:

earth: $1550 + 54$ ADT
gravel: $5200 + 18$ ADT
paved: $10400 + 1$ ADT

These formulas indicate that for traffic volumes up to 100 vehicles a day maintenance costs are lowest on an earth road, for 100–300 vehicles lowest on a gravel road and beyond 300 vehicles lowest on a paved road.

[6] For details on maintenance, see the special report prepared for the Export-Import Bank by the U.S. Bureau of Public Roads, *Progress Report on the Iranian Highway Maintenance Program*, (1965).

TABLE 12: Typical Road Construction and Consultants' Costs in Iran, 1965—Mountainous Terrain

Surface:	Asphalt					Gravel			
Width:	7 meters			6 meters		7 meters		6 meters	
Maximum axle-load (tons):	14		8	14	8	14	8	14	8
	('000 rials per km)	(% of total)	(7 meter asphalt road, 14 ton axle weight = 100)						
Earth works (incl. clearing & grubbing)	6,000	32.7	100	80	80	100	100	80	80
Sub-base and base, of which	950	5.2	65	85	57	119	83	100	71
Sub-base	225	1.2	—	85	—	100	—	85	—
Base	725	4.0	85	85	75	125	109	105	93
Pavement	1,200	6.5	100	85	85	—	—	—	—
Shoulders	150	.8	100	75	75	100	100	75	75
Culverts and other structures, of which	9,425	51.4	100	98	98	100	100	98	98
Culverts and protection works	4,100	22.3	100	95	95	100	100	95	95
Retaining walls	475	2.6	100	95	95	100	100	95	95
Major bridges	1,600	8.7	100	100	100	100	100	100	100
Tunnels	3,250	17.7	100	100	100	100	100	100	100
Miscellaneous	600	3.2	100	100	100	100	100	100	100
Total contractor costs	18,325	99.8	98	90	89	94	92	85	84
Consultants' fees	3,000	16.3	100	90	90	—	—	—	—
Grand total construction costs	21,325	116.3	98	90	90	94	92	85	84

Source: Kampsax, Tehran.

TABLE 13: Typical Road Construction and Consultants' Costs in Iran, 1965—Normal Terrain

Surface:	Asphalt					Gravel				Earth			
Width:	7 meters			6 meters		7 meters		6 meters		7 meters		6 meters	
Maximum axle-load (*tons*):	14		8	14	8	14	8	14	8	14	8	14	8
	(*'000 rials per km*)	(*% of total*)					*(7 meter asphalt road, 14 ton axle weight = 100)*						
Earth works (incl. clearing & grubbing)	2,564	43.1	100	86	86	100	100	86	86	100	100	86	86
Sub-base and base, of which	1,061	17.8	59	86	51	47	47	41	41	—	—	—	—
Sub-base	472	7.9	—	86	86	100	100	86	86	—	—	—	—
Base	589	9.9	100	86	86	—	—	—	—	—	—	—	—
Pavement	1,294	21.8	100	86	86	—	—	—	—	—	—	—	—
Shoulders	37	.6	100	100	100	100	100	100	100	—	—	—	—
Culverts	606	10.2	100	86	86	100	100	86	86	100	100	86	86
Miscellaneous	385	6.5	100	100	100	100	100	100	100	100	100	100	100
Total contractor costs	5,947	100.0	86	90	78	71	71	65	65	43	43	39	39
Consultants' fee	595	10.0	100	80	80	78	78	74	74	59	59	52	52
Grand total construction costs	6,542	110.0	88	89	78	72	72	67	67	45	45	41	41
Annual maintenance costs	60	1.0	100	90	90	57	57	50	50	43	43	39	39

Sources: Ammann & Whitney, Tehran; Ministry of Roads, Tehran.

TABLE 14: Typical Road Construction and Consultants' Costs in Iran, 1965—Flat or Rolling Terrain

Surface:	Asphalt					Gravel			
Width:	7 meters			6 meters		7 meters		6 meters	
Maximum axle-load (tons):	14		8	14	8	14	8	14	8
	('000 rials per km)	(% of total)	(7 meter asphalt road, 14 ton axle weight = 100)						
Earth works (incl. clearing & grubbing)	1,100	100	100	85	85	100	100	85	85
Sub-base and base, of which	1,075	100	59	85	51	117	73	99	63
Sub-base	350	7.1	—	85	—	100	—	85	—
Base	725	14.6	88	85	75	125	109	105	93
Pavement	1,200	24.3	100	85	85	—	—	75	75
Shoulders	150	3.0	100	75	75	100	100	90	90
Culverts	1,100	22.2	100	90	90	100	100	100	100
Miscellaneous	325	6.6	100	100	100	100	100		
Total contractor costs	4,950	100.0	91	88	81	80	70	69	62
Consultants' fee	800	16.2	91	88	81	80	70	69	62
Grand total construction costs	5,750	116.2	91	88	81	80	70	69	62

Source: Kampsax, Tehran.

V

TRAFFIC STRUCTURE AND GROWTH

The purpose of improving a road is to provide economic benefits, which accrue through usage over time. So the benefits which derive from savings in road user costs (to be considered in Chapter VI) depend first, on the volume of traffic in the base year, and next on the growth of the traffic. However, this road project in Iran was finished, for the most part, only in 1961–63. The year 1965 therefore offered a rather poor perspective for estimating traffic growth over the full lifetime of the roads, presumably stretching into the 1980's.

Detailed traffic counts had been made in Iran in the years 1960–62, but were unfortunately discontinued thereafter. For some roads "pre-project" traffic data were also available for 1958–59. Supplementary information on traffic was available from registers kept by truck-weighing stations on the main highways, data on fuel consumption and vehicle registration, import-export statistics for Khoramshahr port and data on rail freight movements.

The analysis of available data was carried out with several objectives in mind. First, there was a need to find out how actual transport flows related to the project roads. Second, the authors hoped the data would shed some light on economic issues such as road-rail competition. Third, indications of future traffic growth were sought as a basis for cost-benefit calculations. A more thorough discussion of the authors' analysis, along with additional data, is given in Annex I.

Estimating the Volume of Traffic

The Traffic Counts

The purpose of a traffic survey is, of course, to provide data of traffic flows on individual roads. In the government surveys of 1960–62, average daily traffic (ADT) counts were derived, in principle, from four counting periods of three days each. At each observation point, traffic (for both directions combined) was differentiated into eleven vehicle types. Arrangements for the traffic counts were made by the provinces under the auspices of the Ministry of Roads.

Analysis of the traffic count data reveals some rather serious deficiencies. In some instances, information is obviously wrong; in others, figures are identical to those of previous years, which may mean a new count was not taken; in still others, details and totals do not match. For the purposes of this study, such data have been suitably adjusted or omitted altogether. The recorded traffic flows on some roads, such as Hamadan–Khosravy (Road I), seem high compared with the visual impressions of the authors during a tour of the project roads in 1965.

To minimize the influence of errors, the detailed counts have been aggregated according to project roads, (except that no information is available for the Shahabad–Malavi road, Road II). Moreover, the ADT figures by road and vehicle type have been calculated as an annual average for the three years 1960–62, to reduce the impact of sometimes erratic fluctuations in the original annual data. The results are shown in Table 15.

Average daily traffic data for the project roads as a group—weighted by road length—amounted to 569 vehicles: 41 percent passenger cars and pickup trucks, 39 percent two-axle trucks, and 20 percent three-axle trucks. Casual observation by the authors

42

TABLE 15: Traffic Count Information on the Project Roads, 1960-1962

Road	Length (kms)	Total		Average Daily Traffic					
							Vehicle Types		
		1960–62	1962	I	II	III 1960–62	I	II	III
				(number of vehicles)			(percentage structure)		
I Hamadan–Khosravy	371	554	589	238	216	100	43	39	18
II Shahabad–Malavi	158	..	..	..	..	..	..	..	..
III Kermanshah–Saghez	306	244	265	112	78	54	46	32	22
IV Divandareh–Bijar[a]	55	87	103	29	37	21	33	42	25
V Rudehen–Babol	156	691	627	380	242	69	55	35	10
VI Khoramshahr–Andimeshk	283	903	1,002	370	334	199	41	37	22
VII Ahwaz–Sar Bandar	157	406	298	203	166	37	50	41	9
VIII Avadj–Ghazvin	112	753	873	301	316	136	40	42	18
IX Ghazvin–Bandar Pahlavy	204	858	878	395	352	111	46	41	13
X Avadj–Malayer	202	552	504	182	243	127	33	44	23
XI Malayer–Andimeshk	383	487	599	146	180	161	30	37	33
Total I–XI (excl. II)	2,229	569	599	236	220	113	41	39	20

[a] Refers to 1961 and 1962 only. Information for 1960 is lacking.
.. : not available.
Note: Vehicle types: I. light vehicles including passenger cars and pickups; II, two-axle trucks and tankers, buses and tractors, etc.; III.

three-axle trucks and tankers, including trailers. For location of roads, see Map 2, p. 12.
Source: Semiannual (1960) and annual (1961 and 1962) traffic count data supplied by the Ministry of Roads, Tehran.

43

would suggest that the proportion of the passenger cars and pickup trucks on the open road is less than this 41 percent; possibly because counting stations were concentrated around population centers where there is more local car traffic. Their location also implies that the traffic counts are on the high side as indicators of inter-city traffic. With some exceptions (especially Road V, Rudehen–Babol, where the proportion of passenger cars was notably higher), the traffic composition does not seem to vary widely between different road sections.

The Weighing Stations

The truck-weighing stations collect, *inter alia*, information on origin and destination of the trucks stopped and weighed, the type of truck, the load carried in tons, and the major commodity carried. The limited sample of data collected permits analysis only of traffic flows on the Trans-Iranian highway. The sample does make it possible to piece together a more detailed picture of traffic on this principal traffic artery. Truck transport on the Trans-Iranian highway consists of long-haul trips, about 1,100 kms on the average. Northbound transport is clearly much more important than southbound; traffic originates principally at the main Gulf ports, Khoramshahr and Bandar Shahpoor, and is destined largely for the main population center at Tehran. Changes in the traffic volume between these terminals are small, except at two points, Hamadan, and Ghazvin, where the northbound flow from the Gulf ports is joined by that from the northwest (Tabriz, Rezaiyeh) and from the Caspian (Rasht). The commodity composition of the northbound flow also changes somewhat on its way to Tehran because of inland additions to the flow, mainly food products, especially wheat.

Statistics on rail freight loaded at Khoramshahr, subtracted from import statistics for Khoramshahr, provided another indication of northbound traffic on the main artery. This served as a rough check on the other two independent estimates—traffic count data and weighing station information—of the flow of freight on the sole road northward from Khoramshahr to Ahwaz. Comparison suggests that the information from the weighing stations appreciably underestimates the actual flow of freight over the road (see Annex I, especially Annex Table 4). The usefulness of the weighing station information, at least of the sample used in this study, would therefore seem to be restricted, in principle, to providing an impression of the *structure* of transport. On the other hand, comparison of the north-bound freight traffic estimates derived from the traffic counts with similar estimates reached by subtracting rail freight from imports, would seem to corroborate the authors' impression that the traffic counts overstate the actual traffic movement.

However, following these and other checks on the available data, the authors adopted the traffic count data as the basis for their estimates of traffic volume in the base year. Although these data are certainly not of top quality, they are available for nearly all roads and for several years, and are broken down by category of vehicle. A sensitivity analysis was carried out to consider the effect on returns if actual traffic volume in 1960–62 was 25% less than the traffic count data indicate. This sensitivity analysis is described in Chapter VIII.

As one result of this reappraisal effort, the authors strongly believe that checks and analyses to gain insight into the "quality" or reliability of available data deserve much more attention than they usually receive in practice. The analyst would acquire a better feel for the qualifications and uncertainties surrounding his final conclusions and recommendations and have some basis for rejecting some data while accepting others. In addition, the weaknesses of the data revealed by such tests should form a powerful stimulus for the improvement of data collection.

Truck Traffic Diverted from Rail

The bulk of the growing traffic on the Khoramshahr–Tehran road, as we have seen, is northbound and consists of imports transported from the Gulf ports to the northern population center. Alternative transport is provided by rail. The question therefore is whether the growing truck transport is, or has been, the result of diversion from the railroad. Table 16 shows the shares of rail and road in the transportation of imports inland through Khoramshahr and Bandar Shahpoor, and suggests that the shift from rail to road accelerated somewhat around 1962, coinciding with the completion of the roads.

TABLE 16: Imports Transported from Khoramshahr and Bandar Shahpoor, by Rail and Road, 1959–1964

('000 tons)

	1959	1960	1961	1962	1963	1964
Khoramshahr	730	891	761	832	757	1098
Bandar Shahpoor	428	587	541	435	377	923
Total imports	1158	1478	1302	1267	1134	2021
Index 1959 = 100	100	128	112	109	98	175
Percentage by rail						
Khoramshahr	36.7	30.2	27.4[c]	19.8	17.6	17.4[c]
Bandar Shahpoor	90.0	71.6	89.2	83.4	71.5	65.3
Both	56.8	54.6	53.1	41.7	36.8	39.3
Percentage by road						
Khoramshahr[a]	63.3	69.8	72.6[c]	80.2	80.4	82.6[c]
Bandar Shahpoor[b]	9.1	6.4	10.8	16.6	28.5	34.7
Both	43.2	45.4	46.9	58.3	63.2	60.7

[a] Construction completed: Avadj–Ghazvin, Oct. 1960; Khoramshahr–Andimeshk, March 1961; Malayer–Avadj, Oct. 1962; Andimeshk–Malayer, April 1963.

[b] Construction completed: Sar Bandar–Ahwaz, Sept. 1962.

[c] Hence the apparent transport of freight by road from Khoramshahr was 552,000 tons in 1961, and 907,000 tons in 1964. See Annex Table 4.

Note: Share of rail transport calculated on the basis of tonnage loaded by the railway in the port and the total volume of imports in the port; apparent road transport calculated as the difference between total imports in the port and the volume loaded by the railway.

Sources: For imports, *Bank Markazi Bulletin*, May–June 1965, pages 129–133; for rail statistics, Iranian State Railways, 1965.

This does not necessarily mean, however, that the reconstruction of the road, with the corresponding reduction in trucking rates (see Chapter VI), was the major factor. It could be that this diversion reflected, in part at least, a long-term trend and generally unsatisfactory performance of the railways. A comparison of the development over time of the freight transport by rail (excluding petroleum products) originating in Khoramshahr and Bandar Shahpoor with overall rail transport in Iran was inconclusive.[1] The effect of road improvements on the share of the two ports in rail traffic is swamped by fluctuations in the volume of imports, especially through Bandar Shahpoor. On balance, the available evidence would seem to support a conclusion that the reconstruction of the road did accelerate the diversion of traffic from rail to road.

---

[1] See Table 24, p. 62, for rate comparisons.

Traffic Growth

Vehicle registration and fuel consumption[2] data over time give a fair indication of the overall development of traffic in a country. As Tables 17 and 18 show, total vehicle registrations in Iran rose by over 10 percent annually during the period 1958–63, and fuel consumption by somewhat less than 10 percent per year. However, these overall rates conceal widely divergent rates for passenger cars and trucks and for gasoline and diesel oil; passenger car registration increased 12.8 percent per year, truck registration only 5.1 percent. It is apparently contradictory that gasoline consumption grew only some 6 percent annually while diesel oil consumption rose by 18 percent per year. Possible causes for this divergence include the increasing use of diesel engines in both trucks and passenger cars, heavier trucks, which are mainly diesel-fueled, and a parallel increase in the annual mileage of the average truck. The lack of more detailed statistical material which could shed light on these developments (e.g. registration data on trucks according to size and type of fuel used), rules out further analysis.

TABLE 17: Vehicle Registration, 1958–1963

('000's)

	Passenger Cars	Trucks	Buses	Total	% Increase over Previous Year
1958	67.3	28.5	7.1	102.9	
1959	79.6	31.9	7.4	118.9	15.5
1960	94.3	35.5	8.0	137.8	15.9
1961	97.4	34.3	8.2	139.9	1.5
1962	106.1	35.0	8.4	149.5	6.9
1963	122.4	36.5	10.5	169.4	13.3
Average % annual growth					
1958–63	12.8	5.1	8.0	10.4	

Source: Police Department, Tehran.

---

[2] The fuel consumption data refer to fuel consumption by vehicles only. Especially for diesel oil there may be large differences between total consumption and consumption by vehicles: in Iran, for example, over 60 percent of total diesel oil consumption is for other than vehicle use.

TABLE 18: Fuel Consumption, 1958–1964

('000 cubic meters)

	Gasoline	Diesel Oil	Lubricant Oil	Total	% Increase over Previous Year
1958	522.5	168.8	7.8	699.1	
1959	564.7	225.0	8.1	797.8	14.1
1960	625.7	215.6	8.8	850.1	6.6
1961	644.9	261.2	10.7	916.8	7.8
1962	663.2	368.9	12.8	1,044.9	13.9
1963	702.3	381.9	8.3	1,092.5	4.6
1964	739.3	469.0	10.8	1,219.1	11.6
Average % annual growth					
1958–63	6.1	17.7	1.0	9.4	
1958–64	5.9	18.5	5.5	9.7	

Source: National Iranian Oil Company, Tehran.

The different growth rates have resulted in a marked increase in the share of passenger cars in the vehicle fleet and of diesel fuel in fuel consumption:

	1958	1963	1964
	(percentage shares)		
Vehicles			
Passenger cars	65.4	72.3	..
Trucks	27.7	21.5	..
Buses	6.9	6.2	..
Total	100	100	..
Fuel			
Gasoline	75	64	61
Diesel oil	24	35	38
Lubricating oil	1	1	1
Total	100	100	100

The composition of the registered vehicle fleet in 1961 was passenger cars (69%), trucks (25%) and buses (6%). The traffic count on project roads (1960–62) showed, as might be expected, a substantially different distribution—passenger cars and pickups (41%), two-axle trucks and tankers, buses and tractors etc. (39%), three-axle trucks and tankers, including trailers (20%). Two probable explanations are a) passenger cars and buses tend to operate more in urban centers, and trucks less, and b) trucks, especially heavy trucks, have a much higher annual mileage than cars and are therefore more frequently seen in traffic counts.

48

The combined evidence of the vehicle registration data and fuel consumption data may be interpreted as suggesting that inter-city traffic of passenger cars and light gasoline-fueled trucks (pickups) has grown by somewhat less than 12.8 percent p.a., say 10 percent, whereas the average annual mileage of heavier trucks has increased gradually, in line with the gradual increase in gross vehicle weights.[3] Therefore an annual increase of the heavier trucks in inter-city traffic of somewhat more than 5 percent, say 7 percent, would seem indicated.

These overall data, relating to possible national trends, may or may not be indicative for specific roads. Attempts to establish a closer link with traffic developments on the project roads, by studying regional registration and fuel consumption data, failed. First, there were differences in coverage between the regional registration and fuel consumption data. Second, the relationship between registration and fuel consumption differed from one region to another. Third, even if an estimate of regional traffic growth could somehow be arrived at, it would still not distinguish between inter-city (highway) and urban traffic.

Future Growth of Traffic

The major uncertainties in estimating future traffic growth are possible developments affecting transport between the Gulf ports and the northern population centers. In general, it seems reasonable to link the growth of northbound road traffic to the growth of imports. The value of imports is largely a function of oil exports; expansion trends indicate that an increase in oil export value of some 9–10 percent per year is a reasonable expectation. Import tonnage may be expected to rise more slowly, reflecting a gradual shift towards higher-value/lower-volume goods. As Table 19 shows, the composition of Iranian imports allows ample scope for such a shift.

The three principal import commodity groups—iron, sugar and wheat—presently account for some 53 percent of total imports in terms of volume, but only some 15 percent in terms of value. The

---

[3] For the relationship between average annual mileage and gross vehicle weight, see Jan de Weille, *Quantification of Road User Savings*, World Bank Staff Occasional Paper No. 2, (1966), p. 60.

TABLE 19: Imports by Commodity Groups, Volume and Value, 1963

| | Volume | | Value | | Unit Price |
	('000 tons)	(% of total)	(million rials)	(% of total)	('000 rials)
Iron and ironware	374	27.6	4,185	10.7	11.2
Sugar	275	20.3	1,289	3.3	4.7
Wheat	71	5.2	387	1.0	5.5
Sub-total	720	53.1	5,861	15.0	8.1
Medical and chemical preparations	66	4.9	3,573	9.1	54.1
Paper, cardboard, etc.	62	4.6	1,114	2.8	18.0
Machinery and parts	47	3.5	6,105	15.5	129.9
Other products	460	33.9	22,629	57.6	49.2
Total	1,355	100.0	39,282	100.0	29.0

Source: Foreign Trade Statistics of Iran, 1342 P.M., Tehran.

erection of a steel mill in Esfahan, in process in 1968, may reduce the future need for iron and ironware imports, the most important commodity group. Favorable development of sugar and wheat production would also tend to reduce the volume as compared to the value of imports. On balance, it would seem that total import tonnages might grow by no more than some 7 percent per year over the next fifteen years.

Three factors might distort a simple relationship between growth of import volume and the volume of transport on the Khoramshahr/Bandar Shahpoor–Tehran route. First, a possible shift might take place in the relative importance of Khoramshahr/Bandar Shahpoor as ports of entry. Iran's foreign trade statistics for 1963 show that some 75 percent of the volume of Iranian imports, and 70 percent of their value, originate in Western and Eastern Europe. Following the agreement between the U.S.S.R. and Iran on shipments via the Volga/Don Canal, imports might shift to some extent in the future from the southern ports to the northern ports. But it is too early to judge. Until recently, the northern ports have handled less than 6 percent (1964) of total Iranian port traffic. Consequently, even a considerable relative increase would only mildly affect the southern ports; in fact, if the diversion through the northern ports were to increase by, say, 50 percent, the corresponding decrease in traffic through the southern ports would be less than 3 percent.

Secondly, the position of the Persian Gulf ports might be affected by the development of Bandar Abbas in the southeast, partly for strategic/political reasons. The impact on import traffic via Khoramshahr, if any, will probably be small. The port activities in Bandar Abbas will presumably be mainly regional in character, at least in the foreseeable future. The travelling distance between Bandar Abbas and Tehran is some 1,580 kms as compared with about 1,110 kms from Khoramshahr to Tehran now and only some 930 kms after the road connection Burujird–Qum–Tehran has been improved (see p. 16).

Thirdly, the share of rail transport in imports through Khoramshahr/Bandar Shahpoor may change. A well-founded judgment regarding the future competitive position of the railways would require an analysis of the present position and potentialities of the Iranian State Railways, which is beyond the scope of the present study. On available evidence, however, it seems likely that the existing downward trend in the relative importance of rail transport will continue.

On balance, therefore, a future annual growth rate of around 7 percent in the volume of truck transport on the Trans-Iranian highway seems reasonable. The estimated past growth rate of 7 percent for heavy trucks and 10 percent for cars and light trucks, in conjunction with the 60–40 ratio of heavy to light vehicles in the 1961 traffic composition, suggests an overall traffic rate of growth of over 8 percent.

The road user savings calculations in Chapter VI will be based on an assumption of a constant traffic composition. But we have seen that there has been a gradual shift towards lighter vehicles, for which costs and savings are lower. To take account of the probability that this trend will continue, we shall choose in the road user savings calculation a conservative growth rate estimate of 7.5 percent for traffic on the project roads.

VI

ROAD USER SAVINGS AND TRUCKING RATES

Among their major benefits, road improvements are commonly expected to produce road user savings. Savings are estimated from the calculation of road user costs. The original appraisal report of May 1959 anticipated such savings but, contrary to the practice now current in the Bank, did not quantify these benefits in any detail. In this study, road user costs and savings have been estimated along the lines set forth at length in an earlier Bank staff study, *Quantification of Road User Savings*, which will be hereafter referred to as QRUS.[1] Road user costs for this purpose have a specific sense. They are a concept for measuring savings resulting from a specific improvement on a specific road. The measuring unit is the total cost of operating a vehicle at a certain speed on a certain type of road; it includes only those costs which are affected by the quality improvement of the road. Others, such as the costs of loading and unloading, overhead costs, stopping, taxes, levies, duties, etc., are excluded, as there are no savings on these costs to enter into the savings benefits of the project.

Road user costs as used here should not be confused with average trucking costs as usually understood in everyday life. These refer

---

[1] Jan de Weille, *op. cit.*

to the average costs to the trucker of running his truck(s) on all sorts of roads and in varying operating conditions. They cover the average total costs of trips, including loading and unloading, on different roads, and allow for overheads. The average trucking costs concept (excluding taxes) enters into this study as an approximate measure of benefits from shortened travelling distances.[2] The relations between the concepts and estimates of road user savings, average trucking costs, and rates are discussed in more detail in Annex II.

Finally, there are other savings which can result from road improvements, related to such costs as damage and spoilage of goods, accidents, time, etc. Some of these savings are taken into account in the calculation of road user savings, others are not. As a group, they are discussed in this chapter under the generic term "associated cost savings."

Road User Costs and Savings

There were not as many difficulties as might have been expected in adapting the QRUS material. Iran 1965 price levels, taken before tax, were not too different, except in the case of wages, from the "indicative prices" in that study. Passenger vehicle types corresponded closely enough, but it was necessary to make adjustments for the different trucks used in Iran and for diesel oil consumption instead of gasoline. Perhaps the biggest difference was the much longer truck lifetime—twenty years—assumed in Iran than in the QRUS. This affected the depreciation calculation. The arithmetic is described in detail in Annex II.

The resulting unit road user costs and savings—for four types of vehicle on three types of road—are summarized in Table 20; details are given in Annex Table 5. Road user costs for passenger cars on paved roads, for example, amount to Rials 2.56 and Rials 3.57

---

[2] In principle, road user savings on account of quality improvement of a road could also be estimated on the basis of average costs if data on costs per trip (excluding overheads and taxes) were available by type of road. Such data are seldom available. The *level* of such average trip costs per km would, of course, exceed road user costs, as defined here, but the *difference* in costs on different types of road— the road user savings—would be the same, in principle, as the estimate arrived at by the method used here.

TABLE 20: Summary of Road User Costs and Savings, 1965
(excluding taxes)

Road User Costs

Type of Road	Speed		Type of Vehicle			
			Passenger Cars		Trucks	
	Passenger	Trucks	Small	Large	Two-axle	Three-axle
	(km/hr)		*(rials per 1000 km)*			
Paved	80	72	2,563	3,570	4,804	6,959
Gravel	64	56	3,300	4,583	7,119	10,638
Earth	56	48	4,084	5,782	11,402	17,911
			(US dollars per 1000 km)			
Paved	80	72	34.17	47.60	64.03	92.76
Gravel	64	56	44.00	61.11	94.90	141.80
Earth	56	48	54.45	77.09	151.99	238.76

Road User Savings

Road Improvement from						
			(rials per km)			
Gravel to paved			.74	1.02	2.32	3.68
Earth to gravel			.78	1.20	4.28	7.27
Earth to paved			1.52	2.21	6.60	10.95
			(US cents per km)			
Gravel to paved			.98	1.35	3.09	4.91
Earth to gravel			1.05	1.60	5.71	9.69
Earth to paved			2.03	2.95	8.80	14.60
			(rials per capacity ton-km)			
Gravel to paved					.22	.25
Earth to gravel					.41	.49
Earth to paved					.63	.73

Note: The savings presented in this table refer only to those resulting from upgrading 1 km of earth (gravel) road to 1 km of gravel (paved) road.

Source: See Annex Table 5, p. 117.

per km for Volkswagen type and Mercedes 190SL type cars respectively. Corresponding figures for the two-axle and three-axle trucks are Rials 4.80 and Rials 6.96 per km. These road user costs are *not* the average cost of year-round truck operation. They relate instead to running costs at specific speeds, on level roads without curves, and at prices excluding taxes. The road user savings thus calculated do not reflect the impact of lesser gradients and easier curves.[3] However, the QRUS study suggests that these factors are generally of only minor importance for larger road segments.[4] With these

---

[3] The cost-benefit calculations of Chapter VIII, however, do take account of shortened travelling distances.

[4] QRUS, p. 40; see also Chapter VII of this study.

qualifications, the unit costs of Table 20 provide relevant measures for the economic evaluation of the road user savings benefits from the project. They are shown graphically in Chart 2.

Average Year-Round Costs

Average trucking cost, when related to average rate, indicates whether the trucker makes a loss or profit. It is thus a financial concept for which data can be solicited from people in the trucking industry. The authors obtained information from a medium-sized trucking firm, various experts in and suppliers to the industry, and two industrial firms which operate their own trucking fleets. The resulting data on trucking costs are limited to operations mainly on good and well-maintained paved highways. But they are useful to us for two reasons. First of all, as already pointed out, average year-round costs provide a better approximation of savings from shortened routes than do road user savings. Secondly, the trucking costs provide a cross-check for the road user savings calculated above and derived from QRUS. Detailed comparisons of road user costs and average trucking costs are given in Annex II, which also compares average trucking costs and rates. These comparisons suggest that the various cost and rate estimates in this study are broadly consistent with each other, although the road user cost estimates (derived from QRUS) are perhaps somewhat on the low side.

By way of illustration, Table 21 summarizes average trucking costs and road user costs for two types of truck, two-axle 10.5-ton and three-axle 15-ton. The large difference between the cost figures reflects the difference in concepts. As a measure of savings from shortened travelling distances, the average trucking costs must be adjusted for the tax component. The average trucking costs of, respectively, Rials 7.76 and Rials 9.91 per vehicle-km (i.e. excluding taxes) give a measure of the cost savings from a reduction in travelling distance of 1 km for the two types of truck.

Corresponding data on year-round costs of operating passenger cars in Iran are not available. Moreover, the year-round costs for passenger cars would probably largely refer to in-city driving,

CHART 2

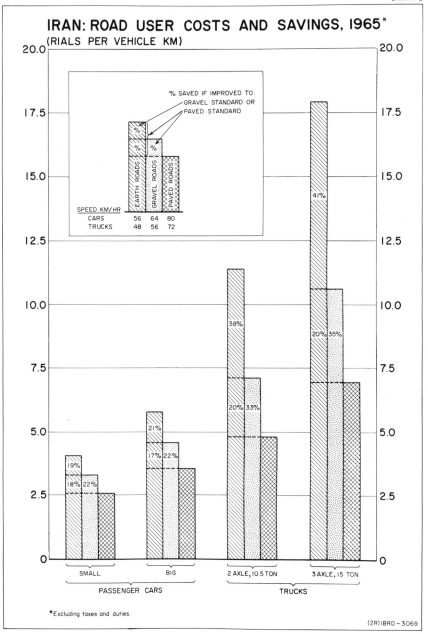

IRAN: ROAD USER COSTS AND SAVINGS, 1965*
(RIALS PER VEHICLE KM)

% SAVED IF IMPROVED TO:
GRAVEL STANDARD OR
PAVED STANDARD

EARTH ROADS
GRAVEL ROADS
PAVED ROADS

SPEED KM/HR			
CARS	56	64	80
TRUCKS	48	56	72

SMALL

BIG

PASSENGER CARS

2 AXLE, 10.5 TON

3 AXLE, 15 TON

TRUCKS

19%
18% 22%

21%
17% 22%

38%
20% 33%

41%
20% 35%

*Excluding taxes and duties.

(2R) IBRD-3069

TABLE 21: Comparison of Average Trucking and Road User Costs

(on paved roads, rials per vehicle-km)

| Type of Truck | Average Trucking Costs | | Road User Costs |
	including taxes	excluding taxes	excluding taxes
Two-axle, 10.5 ton	8.73	7.76	4.80
Three-axle, 15 ton	11.26	9.91	6.96

Source: See Annex II, p. 123.

whereas we want to establish the savings from a reduction in travelling distance on between-city roads. However, if the difference between year-round costs and road user costs for trucks is indicative of the order of magnitude, the user cost data for passenger cars given previously can be adjusted to indicate savings from shortened travelling; the result, per vehicle-km on paved roads, is Rials 3.89 for small passenger cars, and Rials 5.36 for large passenger cars. Anyway, passenger cars account for only some two-fifths of all traffic counted on the project roads, and the savings for a passenger car are significantly lower than those for trucks. Even if road user costs for passenger cars were only 25 percent of year-round costs, the ultimate savings from a shorter distance for all traffic (of average composition) would be reduced by less than 5 percent.

Actually, estimates of savings from reduction in distance, on the basis of average costs, will tend to be on the high side because not all costs vary proportionately with the number of kilometers travelled; and some costs, such as loading and unloading costs, will not vary at all with distance. On balance, overestimation on account of this factor is likely to be small. An opposite tendency toward underestimation exists in estimates of costs and therefore savings from road quality improvement, because all relevant factors are not fully taken into account. The extent of the distortion for both cases seems to be relatively small.

Changes in Trucking Rates

Available data relate mainly to the Khoramshahr–Tehran route. Table 22 shows trucking rates on this route from 1961 to 1965 for the ten most important commodities (or groups of commodities) transported from the south to Tehran. These rates are established by the Khoramshahr Trucking Syndicate in cooperation with the Khoramshahr Chamber of Commerce. The average trucking rate, as derived from those ten commodities, amounted to some Rials 1,500 per ton (or about Rials 1.35 per capacity ton-km).[5] There was relatively little change over the five years.

TABLE 22:   Trucking Rates, Khoramshahr–Tehran, 1961–65

(rials per ton)

	1961	1962	1963	1964	1965	Average 1961–65
Tools	1,600	1,650	1,600	1,600	1,475	1,585
Cables	1,600	1,600	1,600	1,550	1,550	1,580
Iron beams (12m)	1,200	1,280	1,050	1,000	1,265	1,159
Iron beams (14m)	1,250	1,440	1,200	1,000	1,395	1,257
Electric wire	1,500	1,550	1,600	1,550	1,575	1,530
Water piping equipment	1,500	1,500	1,400	1,250	1,475	1,535
Equipment for heavy machinery	1,600	1,650	1,600	1,400	1,685	1,587
Electric equipment	1,870	1,650	1,700	1,600	1,700	1,704
Tubes	1,500	1,500	1,400	1,500	1,475	1,476
Foodstuffs	1,700	1,800	1,700	1,700	1,700	1,720
Average[a]	1,532	1,567	1,485	1,410	1,522	1,503
Average of five-year period = 100	102	104	99	94	101	100

[a] This is a simple average of the rates for the ten commodity groups. Calculation of a weighted average on the basis of the commodity composition of the northbound transport flow (see Annex Table 2, p. 106) would of course, have been preferable, but is not possible due to the large "miscellaneous" commodity group, comprising some 50 percent of the total. In this particular case, however, the choice of weighting system makes little difference because of the limited spread of the individual rates.

Source: Khoramshahr Trucking Syndicate, and Khoramshahr Chamber of Commerce.

Under competitive transport conditions, the benefits from a road improvement would be reflected in a fall in trucking rates. At first sight, rates do not seem to reflect lower road user costs, although there was some decline in relation to the general price level—both the cost of living and the wholesale index rose during this period by about 7 percent.[6] It might be that rates had already come down by 1961, the first year of the statistical series, following partial completion of some of the project roads. Unfortunately, because the Khoramshahr Trucking Syndicate was only established in 1960/61, strictly comparable data on rates are not available prior to 1961.

[5] Given the 100 percent load factor on this route, ton-km rates equal capacity ton-km rates.

[6] Source: *IMF International Financial Statistics.*

Information supplied by a major transport firm, however, suggests that rates were substantially higher in the period 1958–60 than in 1961–65:

TABLE 23: Sample Trucking Rates, Khoramshahr–Tehran, 1958–60

Commodity	Rials per ton
Iron beams/bars	1,800–2,100
Machinery	1,800–2,000
Electrical cables	1,700–1,800
General cargo	1,800–2,000
Average (unweighted)	1,775–1,975 (= 1,875)

Source: Levant Express Transport, Tehran and Khoramshahr, 1965.

On the basis of this evidence, it might be concluded that by 1961 rates had come down by some 20 percent on the Khoramshahr–Tehran route. By the end of 1961, some 44 percent of the total length of the Khoramshahr–Ghazvin road had been completed. Relatively little work remained to be done during the later stages of construction of the unfinished roads (see Chart 1). It seems reasonable, therefore, to infer that the reduction in rates on the Khoramshahr–Tehran route around 1960/61 does reflect the improvement in road conditions. There was a further decline in rates in 1963–64, when the bulk of the remaining roads were finished. The subsequent increase in 1965 may reflect the increase in import duties on trucks from 15 to 35 percent.

The rate changes for the main import route would not necessarily be indicative, however, of the change in the average rate. Unfortunately, information on truck charges on other routes is even scantier.[7] The available data hardly permit a firm conclusion as to aver-

---

[7] Some rather inconclusive data were obtained during interviews. These are verbal reports on trucking rates "before" and "after" roads had been reconstructed:

From	To	Commodity	Before	After
			Road Improvement	
			(rials per ton-km)	
Shiraz	Tehran	Not specified	0.65–1.41	0.65–0.87
Kermanshah	Tehran	Not specified	1.42	0.76–1.33
Hamadan	Tehran	Cucumbers	1.52	1.19–2.08

Source: Interviews in Shiraz, Kermanshah and Hamadan.

age rate changes on round-trip journeys, direct or indirect, between Khoramshahr and Tehran. However, the imbalance between north and southbound traffic described in Chapter V, reflected in an even larger difference in rates, results in movements in average rates being dominated by the northbound rate. If the northbound rates fell by some 20 percent in 1960/61, or Rials 0.35 per ton-km, the decline in average round trip rates is likely to have been on the order of 17–19 percent. In terms of capacity ton-kms, taking account of the average load factor, this amounts to some Rials 0.17–0.19 on the round trip.[8]

Truck and Rail Rates

As the main road Khoramshahr–Tehran (1,109 kms) runs largely parallel to a rail connection (944 kms), it is interesting to compare respective truck and rail rates on this route. Average rail rates have been calculated using the same commodity groups used for average trucking rates in Table 22. The comparison of rates in Table 24, crude as it is, indicates that, allowing for the difference in rail and road distance, rail and road rates between Khoramshahr and Tehran have been roughly equal since 1961; prior to that, in 1958–60, road rates exceeded rail rates by some 20 percent. However, rail rates are station-to-station while truck rates are door-to-door, and transport by rail in Iran takes much longer than by truck. In view of these differences in quality of service, truck transport is more attractive, at equal rates per ton, than rail transport. Before the reconstruction of the Trans-Iranian highway, and the lowering of trucking rates, this service advantage was, to some extent at least, compensated by the lower direct cost of transport by rail.

These changes in relative rates presumably had some bearing on the disparate development of road and rail transport discussed in

---

[8] The final progress report of October 7, 1964 commented: "The rates charged by these commercial carriers on the improved roads were just about halved compared with the level prevailing before the improvement . . . truck charges fell from Rials 2.50 per ton-km to Rials 1.25." According to the appraisal report of May 1959, "The rates usually charged for road transport . . . range from US cents 1.6–2.8 per ton kilometer," i.e. Rials 1.2–2.1 per ton-km. These figures for average rates prior to improvement of roads appear rather high compared with the figures quoted in Table 23 of only some Rials 1,875 per ton even on the high-rate Khoramshahr-Tehran route, i.e. Rials 1.70 per ton-km at 100 percent load factor.

TABLE 24:   Comparison of Road and Rail Rates

(rials per ton)

Year	Per km		Khoramshahr–Tehran		
	Rail	Road	Rail	Road	
					(rail = 100)
1958–1960	1.64	1.69	1,548	1,875	121
1961	1.64	1.38	1,548	1,532	98
1962	1.64	1.41	1,548	1,567	101
1963	1.64	1.34	1,548	1,485	96
1964	1.56	1.27	1,473	1,410	96
1965	1.56	1.37	1,473	1,522	103

Note: The average rail rate is a simple average of the rates for the ten commodity groups; the rates for each commodity group again are simple averages of the rates for a few representative commodities within each group. See also note to Table 22.

Source: Iranian State Railways; Tables 22 and 23.

Chapter V, p. 45. The reaction of the railways to these adverse developments has until recently been mild. In 1964 the state-owned organization reduced rates by some 5 percent, yet this was not sufficient to change appreciably the competitive position with the roads. In mid-1966, large rail rate reductions of up to 50 percent were introduced, differentiated according to commodity and volume (with minimum cargoes from 1,000 tons to 10,000 tons), and subject in some cases to a minimum distance of 300 kms. It appears, though, that these discounts mainly apply to exports through Khoramshahr and other southern ports (with lower discounts for exports through Julfa in the northwest). According to the *Kayhan Journal* of Tehran (July 2, 1966), the reductions were decreed to help exporters, but also to shift freight back to the railways. Rates on northbound traffic from Khoramshahr/Bandar Shahpoor were apparently not affected. Relative rates per ton should move further against the railways with the reconstruction of the Burujird–Qum shortcut between Tehran and the Gulf ports.

Associated Cost Savings

Apart from road user savings, other cost savings are frequently associated with improved roads. The main examples are: less damage to goods in transit, fewer accidents, shorter time in transit for goods and thus interest savings, time savings of passengers, and less spoilage during lengthy transit. The importance of these factors varies with circumstances, of course, and their quantification raises even greater difficulties—both theoretical and practical—than do road user savings benefits.

The reduction in *damage* to goods during transport clearly depends on the nature of the goods. Heavy iron beams, or wheat, are unlikely to suffer from transport on rough roads. The bulk of truck transport in Iran, in fact, consists of low value bulk commodities (see Annex I), so benefits from reduced damage should be small. Even for highly breakable items such as bottles, this factor may be less important than sometimes thought. A letter to the authors from the Zamzam Bottling Co., Tehran, supplied a realistic example. "A trailer (five-axle) with a load of 1,000 cases of 24 bottles of Pepsi Cola travelling 600 kms on a dirt road would reach the destination with 150–250 broken bottles, whereas on an asphalt road the damage would be 10–20 bottles." This works out at an extra breakage of about one-third bottle per km on the dirt road. In other words (for a five-axle truck) breakage savings per vehicle-km from improvement of the dirt to an asphalt road are worth about 1 rial as compared to some 20 rials in road user savings.

The authors tried to obtain data on changes over time in *accident* rates on the project roads, but without success.

Greater speed has several effects. Its significance for possible *interest* savings on goods in transit may be illustrated by the following example, also taken from the Zamzam letter: "It takes 12–14 hours for a truck to travel a distance of 600 kms (from Tehran to Tabriz) on an asphalt road, whereas the same distance travelled on a dirt road would take 18–20 hours." Interest savings due to shorter transit time were calculated for low value commodities (barley and wheat) and for high value commodities (ghee and butter). Table 25 indicates that even for high value products, at a 10 percent rate of interest, shorter transit time results only in an insignificant saving of interest costs. It amounts to less than 2.5 percent of road user savings per capacity ton-km (from earth to paved).

Time savings of passengers are taken into account in the calculation of road user savings (see Annex II, p. 119). Clearly such time savings have economic value, at least for some persons. However,

TABLE 25: Interest Savings Related to Transit Time

Costs and Savings *(at 10 percent interest)*	Commodities	
	Barley/Wheat	Ghee/Butter
Price per kg.	8	150
Interest costs p.a., per ton	800	15,000
Interest costs per 19 hours (earth road)	1.73	32.53
Interest costs per 13 hours (paved road)	1.19	22.25
Interest savings if road is improved from earth to paved	0.54	10.28
Interest savings if road is improved from earth to paved (per ton-km)	.0009	.0171

there is great uncertainty as to both the passenger hours saved and the appropriate value to be put on time savings of all kinds of passengers (businessmen, officials, friends, children, visitors, etc.).

Finally, greater speed widens the *market* for some commodities; for example, perishables may spoil before they reach the market if transport is slow. This affects only a minor part of the commodities transported by truck in Iran, which as we have seen, consist mainly of bulk goods. Furthermore, many perishables reach their market over relatively short distances—for example, fresh produce from the Caspian Littoral moving to Tehran over the Amol–Babol–Tehran road—so that the impact of time savings on spoilage would in any case be small. The wider aspects of the importance of better roads for agricultural development are considered further in the next chapter.

VII

DEVELOPMENT BENEFITS

In addition to producing road user savings, as discussed in the previous chapter, cheaper transport is frequently credited with development benefits: that is, a reduction in transport costs may stimulate production in agriculture or industry. In principle, there are several ways of measuring such induced benefits. For instance, one might attempt to measure the development benefits directly in terms of increases in the net value of agricultural (and industrial) output, consumer surplus, changes in land rents, etc. Alternatively, and equivalently, one may measure these benefits in terms of the development traffic generated by the lowering of transport costs.

As shown graphically in Chart 3, the total benefits from a road improvement project can be fully measured by the sum of road user savings and development benefits.[1] Schematically, the total benefits from a road project may be represented in terms of transport costs per ton-km (left scale), transport volume (bottom scale), and demand for transport (a straight line function in this chart). Now, as a result of certain road improvements, say that transport costs

---

[1] Possible savings from lower road maintenance costs are omitted in this discussion.

per ton-km go down by AB (left scale). The volume of transport which would take place even without the improvements (usually referred to as the "normal" traffic) is OC (bottom scale); and the total cost savings of this "normal" traffic are therefore OC × AB, i.e. the rectangle ABEF. In addition, the reduction in transport costs induces additional traffic CD ("generated" or "development" traffic) that otherwise would not have taken place. This demand in effect assumes that the reduction in transport costs (AB) is passed on to the shippers/producers. The benefits of this additional traffic are measured by the triangle EGF. There are no additional development benefits from e.g. higher agricultural output or land rents as such. These are already fully accounted for in the development traffic benefits and should not be counted twice.[2]

The specific question remains: have there been any identifiable development benefits since the project was completed? Improvement of the project roads in Iran was expected to have substantial development benefits. In the words of the appraisal report of May 1959, "the proposed improvement and extension of the national road system would materially improve this [unsatisfactory transport] situation for those farmers with reasonable access to the highways concerned. Many of them would fairly rapidly take advantage of better marketing opportunities by diversifying their production with cash cropping. In addition, the improvement of communications would greatly facilitate the increasing efforts of agricultural extension agents to improve farming practices and increase yields. It does not seem unreasonable to expect that as the result of these influences the annual gross value of agricultural production in the regions concerned would increase by at least 5 percent within five years after the completion of the present project; this increase would be of the order of 15 percent to 20 percent of the estimated cost of the roads." The report went on to say that "a preliminary appraisal indicates that a relatively modest additional investment

---

[2] A full discussion of these questions of the measurement of benefits from transport projects is outside the scope of this study and has been given elsewhere. This simplified account is only intended to give some indication to the reader unfamiliar with the subject. The discussion here is in terms of development traffic; similar questions arise with traffic diverted from alternative transport modes or routes to the same destination.

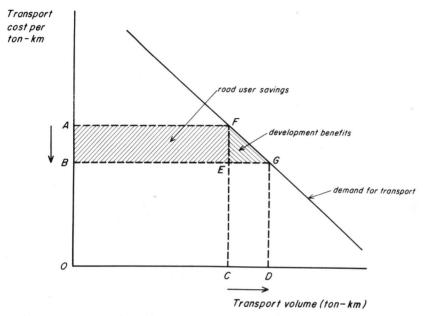

CHART 3

BENEFITS OF A ROAD PROJECT

(R)IBRD-3851

in feeder roads branching from the roads included in the project into the most promising adjacent farming areas should lead to a much greater increase in agricultural production."

Agricultural Benefits

The final progress report on the project, dated October 1964, states: "The effects of road improvement on the economic growth of the service areas is difficult to present in quantitative terms. Moreover, as the Project is only now being completed, it is still too early to discern its full effects." This statement reflects one of the basic difficulties of project (re)appraisal, set forth in Chapter I: the point in time has a bearing on the assessment of benefits. The 1964 report, apparently relying on the observations of Bank and FAO agricultural experts, noted that . . . "in the areas served by many of those roads opened to traffic earlier, there have been not only a

67

large expansion of the areas of agricultural cultivation, but also a considerable diversification of farming, which includes a switch to cash crop growing from the traditional staple crops." The report continued "The Bank's and FAO's agricultural experts considered most of these areas to have high priority for feeder road investment and many of these areas were included in a proposed feeder road project appraised simultaneously with the project supervision mission on the First and Second Road Projects. It may therefore be reasonable to conclude that with an adequate provision of feeder roads under the proposed new project, the economic potentials of the areas served by the Project roads will be adequately exploited."

Unfortunately, the authors found little clear evidence to verify these earlier observations on agricultural benefits. The time series of agricultural production or of crop area are still not available in sufficient detail to give a clear impression of the possible impact of the improvement of the roads. The only regional data available are through 1964–65 for the province of Kermanshah—an area much too broad to discern any possible influence that cheaper transport may have had. Such as they are, these data show some increase in agricultural production for the province as a whole in the period since 1961/62, when gradual completion and opening of the roads might have been expected to have some stimulating effects on agriculture. It is a moot question, however, whether this increase is the result of recent road improvements or of other factors, in line with a general upward trend in agricultural output. From a trip along nearly all the project roads and, in particular, from interviews with people knowledgeable of the principal areas where agricultural development benefits were expected, such as the Hamadan/Kermanshah area and the Caspian Littoral, the authors did not gain the impression of any significant development effects from the improved roads.

In the absence of conclusive quantitative evidence, the authors looked for indirect evidence of agricultural development benefits from the project. The difference between local market prices in the producing regions and those in the central market of Tehran was analyzed. A narrowing of this price gap, i.e. a decline in transport and distribution costs, presumably would have acted as an incentive to increase output (or shipments of produce formerly consumed in the region itself). While the available price data are spotty, the evidence is worth giving. Changes in wholesale price differentials between selected towns and Tehran are shown in Table 26.

TABLE 26: Wholesale Price Differentials between Tehran and Selected Market Towns, 1960–64[a]

(rials per kg or piece)

Year	Wheat	Barley	Rice (Sadri)	Potatoes	Beans (Dry)	Ghee	Butter	Eggs
Kermanshah								
1960	+0.8	+1.0	−3.0	+3.3	+3.5	+10.0	− 3.0	+0.6
1961	+0.8	+1.2	+1.0	+2.5	+6.0	0.0	−20.0	+0.8
1962[b]	+0.8	+0.4	−8.0	+1.0	+4.0	0.0	− 7.0	+0.9
1963	+0.5	+0.5	−3.5	+1.5	+4.0	+12.0	−35.0	+0.5
1964	+0.9	0.0	0.0	+3.2	+4.5	− 5.0	−30.0	+0.2
Rasht								
1960	−0.3	0.0	+1.0	+3.5	..	+ 5.0	+ 7.0	+0.3
1961	−1.0	0.0	+3.0	+1.0	+1.0	−15.0	−20.0	+0.3
1962[b]	−0.5	−0.5	+6.0	+1.0	+2.0	−23.0	+20.0	+0.7
1963	−0.5	+0.2	+3.0	+1.0	−1.0	+17.0	−20.0	0.0
1964	+0.7	−0.2	+2.5	+2.5	−1.0	+35.0	−15.0	−0.3
Ahwaz								
1960	−0.7	0.0	−3.0	−7.5	−2.0	+16.0	+12.0	+0.3
1961	+0.3	+1.0	−3.0	−3.0	−3.0	+ 5.0	− 9.0	0.0
1962[b]	−1.5	−0.3	−3.0	−1.0	−3.0	+17.0	0.0	+0.4
1963	−0.8	−0.3	−9.0	−4.0	+1.5	+22.0	−35.0	0.0
1964	+0.9	−0.4	+7.0	−1.0	+4.0	+30.0	−15.0	−0.3

[a] Wholesale price differentials as of the end of September (of the years referred to). The price differentials are calculated on the basis of the wholesale price, Tehran, minus the corresponding wholesale price in the respective market towns, both expressed in rials per kg (in the case of eggs, rials per piece).
[b] Week ending October 11.
Source of basic data: Ministry of Agriculture, Department of Agricultural Economics.

In interpreting these wholesale prices, it should be remembered that Tehran is a deficit (import) center for all products listed, while the other market centers are all surplus (export) centers for most products other than rice. Rasht is the market town for the principal rice surplus areas. The results appear rather inconclusive. The principal impression is that the price gaps fluctuate considerably from year to year, suggesting separate rather than well-integrated markets. A clear downward trend in the price gaps between exporting region and importing region, which might reflect lower transport costs, is certainly not apparent.[3]

[3] A similar negative conclusion emerges even more strongly from comparison fo Tehran retail prices and wholesale prices in producing areas.

69

The argument, it should be noted, concerns the price *gap* between the producers' and consumers' markets, not the price levels themselves. The price levels might go up or down, or fluctuate from year to year, reflecting changes in demand and supply conditions, without necessarily changing the price gap. Nor can benefits necessarily be deduced from an increase in supplies. An autonomous rise in urban demand and a corresponding increase in agricultural production would raise the volume of "normal" traffic, important for the assessment of road user savings discussed above, but irrelevant to the assessment of development benefits. These require a *narrowing* of the price gap because of lower transport costs inducing an expansion of agricultural output. It is, of course, possible that in the absence of road improvements, transport costs and rates would have risen because of congestion from growing traffic. In that case a constant transport margin (and price gap) does not necessarily indicate lack of development benefits. This would hardly seem to apply, however, to Iran.

Possible Impact of Marketing System

Why was there no narrowing of the price gap? The first possibility is that the cost of transportation for the shipper did not decline. But we concluded in Chapter VI that trucking rates do seem to have come down in 1961 as a result of the road improvements. Apart from rate reduction, effective transport costs for perishables, such as fruit and vegetables, may also have declined because of less spoilage during transport.

The second possibility is that any reductions in trucking rates were offset by increases in marketing margins. This seems very plausible in view of the very imperfect structure of marketing of agricultural products in Iran. Middlemen of various types are in a strong position both politically and economically. The available literature, here briefly summarized in quotations, bears witness to this feature. "There are a number of marketing problems and shortcomings, the most important of which is the lack of credit. . . . The result is that an average farmer has to depend for credit on middlemen who operate throughout the country. Pre-harvest sales are very common. . . . The produce is sold much before it is ready for harvesting. . . . Naturally, the price offered is very low. . . . Where pre-harvest sales are not common, the rate of interest is very high and ranges from 25 to 75 percent. The middleman is very influential particularly in the fruits and vegetables trade. . . . In practice there are many ways and means by which the seller is deprived of his rightful dues. The number of middlemen is also very large. For instance, in the case of rice, there are seven middlemen besides the functionaries like brokers and weighmen between the producer and the consumer. . . . The Government intervention in the case of wheat is mainly in the interest of the consumer. The Cereal Administration makes purchases of wheat and maintains stocks which are released to bakers to keep the price of bread low in urban areas. Markets are not regulated and market changes and practices are not standardized. Market places are owned by private persons and in a few cases by the Municipalities who exercise a sort of control which does not materially contribute to better market conditions." [4]

This situation is reflected in very wide margins between farm prices and consumer prices in Tehran, the former accounting for only 25–50 percent of the final price.[5] Cost of transport amounts only to some 5–10 percent of the margin between farm and retail prices, which mainly consists of middlemen's costs and profits. This is illustrated in Table 27. While only one or two examples relate to the project areas, there is little reason to think that conditions in those areas are essentially different.

[4] A. Jalali, *Report on the Marketing of Agricultural Produce in Iran*, (Tehran, 1963), processed, pp. i–ii; also see H. S. Lodi, *A Case Study on the Marketing of Wheat and Rice in Iran*, (mimeo), 1962, and again Lodi, "Pre-Harvest Sales of Agricultural Produce in Iran," *FAO Bulletin of Agricultural Economics and Statistics*, (June, 1965), pp. 1–4.

[5] And even less on basis of pre-harvest sales. Lodi, "Pre-Harvest Sales," p. 1, reports: "Generally speaking 20–70 percent of the total production of many crops is sold before harvest. The prices received are, on the whole, 20–40 percent below those obtainable in post-harvest sales. Similarly, the producers' share in the consumer price is only 12–26 percent in pre-harvest but nearly twice as much in post-harvest sales.

TABLE 27: Farm Wholesale and Retail Prices, 1961 and 1962

(percentage of retail price)

	Rice (Sadri), Rasht, 1961	Wheat, W. Prov., 1961	Oranges,[a] Shadad,[b] 1961	Cucumbers, Bandar Abbas, 1962	Eggs, Tabriz, 1961
Farm Price	53.9	56.0	53.3	12.0	40.0
Transport to wholesale markets	0.4		..	..	..
Other costs and charges	2.3	3.4	6.8	0.8	10.0
Middlemen's profits	10.9		..	..	..
Wholesale Price (Local)	67.4	59.4	..	..	..
Transport to Tehran	2.2	1.1	3.3	10.0	6.0
Costs	2.3	4.1[c]	0.8	0.8	2.0
Brokerage and Commissions	4.5		8.0	7.5	2.0
Wholesale profit	10.6	12.3[d]	7.7	43.9	20.0
Wholesale Price (Tehran)	87.0	76.9	80.0	75.0	..
Retail Cost and Margin	13.0	23.1[e]	20.0	25.0	20.0
Retail Price	100.0	100.0	100.0	100.0	100.0

[a] At the time of harvest.
[b] Province of Kerman.
[c] Cost of cleaning, drying, milling.
[d] Millers' profits.
[e] Bakers' cost and profits.
Sources: Jalali, *op. cit.*, pp. 35 ff., and Reza Shakri, *Report on Marketing of Wheat in the Western Provinces*, quoted by Lodi, *A Case Study on the Marketing of Wheat and Rice in Iran.*

With such a structure, the impact of lower trucking rates would be small, even if they were passed on to farmers and/or consumers. Even a reduction in trucking rates as large as say, 50 percent, would then raise producers' prices and/or lower retail prices by only 5 percent or less. Under these circumstances, the effect of lower transport costs in expanding the market or stimulating agricultural output is likely to be small.[6] Furthermore, given a monopolistic marketing structure, any lowering of trucking rates would tend to be absorbed in higher profits for middlemen, rather than passed on to the consumer and producer. Thus the authors are inclined to discount the likelihood that, in such situations, road improvement

---

[6] In terms of the "development benefit triangle" of Chart 3 (p. 67), even if EF is sizeable, EG is small because of the relatively small share of transport cost in the total price.

would have any significant development effects.[7] This opinion also applies to the possibility of benefits from agricultural inputs that might have become cheaper as a result of transport improvements.

Any conclusion as regards Iran can be only tentative. Possibly not enough time has yet elapsed to allow the development benefits to come into effect. The completion of the roads was in 1960–63 and the reappraisal in 1965. The general conclusion, which applies to any country, is firm enough however. In conditions with large monopolistic elements in marketing only few development benefits, if any, should be expected from road improvements and lower transport costs.

The development benefits often hoped for may not be forthcoming in such cases unless the marketing structure is thoroughly overhauled. Indeed, "the development effects" of such an overhaul, even in the absence of road improvements, may be far greater than those that might result from road improvement.

---

[7] In terms of the "development benefit triangle" of Chart 3, EF is zero and so is EG. It should be noticed, however, that in situations with a highly monopolistic marketing structure, a large part of middlemen's charges is likely to represent "profits" rather than any economic costs. Any development traffic which *does* take place in such conditions tends to have a value to the economy as a whole which far exceeds the trucking rates. In fact, its unit value is then more nearly approximated by the price gap between producers' prices and consumer prices, with suitable corrections for real items of marketing costs.

VIII

COST-BENEFIT ANALYSIS OF THE PROJECT

Previous chapters have discussed various aspects of construction and maintenance costs, traffic structure and growth, road user savings and trucking rates, and development benefits. In this chapter these are combined into a cost-benefit analysis of the project. A sensitivity analysis explores the effect of changes in estimates of benefits. Possible alternative investments are considered.

As benefits, only the road user savings are taken into account. Other measurable benefits, such as associated cost savings and development benefits, were found to be negligible compared to the margins of error in the traffic estimates and road user savings. The cost-benefit analysis, therefore, compares the cost of construction and maintenance of the project roads with the estimated road user savings resulting. Road user savings are based on 1965 Iranian prices excluding taxes (see Annex Table 6). Construction costs are actual expenditures during the construction period 1959–65.

As we mentioned in the Introduction, a reappraisal should compare costs and benefits on the basis of "with and without" the project, and not on the basis of "before and after." The benefits in this study are calculated on this "with and without" basis. They are in the form of road user savings and refer to traffic which anyway would have used the roads, even in their old condition.

Basic Costs and Benefit Data

The time pattern of expenditure on construction of the eleven project roads is shown in Table 28. The bulk of the construction expenditures occurred in 1960–62 while the original expectation was that the heaviest concentration would be in 1959–60. Completion dates for each road are summarized in the last column of Table 29.

Relevant *traffic flows* are derived from estimated traffic volumes in the base period, i.e. the year that the construction of the individual roads was terminated and also the first year that benefits were generated, and assumed rates of traffic growth. Although the traffic count data as given in Table 15, p. 43, leave much to be desired, and are probably on the high side, they have been used as a starting point for the traffic projections. These counts, for 1960–62 coincide approximately with the completion dates of the project roads (Table 29). The authors consider 7.5 percent per year the most reasonable rate of traffic growth on the project roads. The authors unfortunately had no basis for differentiating traffic growth rates by road. These are assumed uniform for the project roads.

The traffic capacity limit of the newly (re)constructed roads is estimated at around 2,000 vehicles per day. Capacity refers to the number of traffic units per period beyond which vehicle operating costs begin to rise "significantly" because of congestion.[1] Given the initial traffic volumes, the assumed rate of traffic growth and the lifetime of the project roads, this limit would only be reached in a few cases. Without the road improvement, congestion and the rise in vehicle operating costs would have set in at a lower level of traffic. However, the authors have not attempted to quantify the possible

---

[1] The capacity estimate for Iran is based on the standards in use in Great Britain as given by L. Odier, *The Economic Benefits of Road Construction and Improvements*, (Paris, 1962), p. 29. A capacity of 4,500 P.C.U. (passenger car units) per day for a two-lane highway corresponds to about 2,000 vehicle units in Iran, given the typical traffic composition on the project roads of 40 percent light and 60 percent heavy vehicles, with a conversion factor of three light vehicles equal to one heavy vehicle.

TABLE 28: Total Costs (Construction and Consultants') of the Road Project, by Road and over Time

(million rials)

Road	Length (kms)	Per Km	Total 1958–64	1958	1959	1960	1961	1962	1963	1964
A. Actual Costs[a]										
I Hamadan–Khosravy	371	5.1	1,888	293	631	429	398	137	—	—
II Shahabad–Malavi	158	5.7	905	—	128	200	138	136	303	—
III Kermanshah–Saghez	306	3.8	1,154	—	—	204	439	511	—	—
IV Divandareh–Bijar	55	2.5	135	—	10	31	77	17	—	—
V Rudehen–Babol	156	14.1	2,203	—	130	297	478	1,088	210	—
VI Khoramshahr–Andimeshk	283	6.6	1,872	—	187	966	719	—	—	—
VII Ahwaz–Sar Bandar	157	5.7	888	—	—	—	298	595	—	—
VIII Avadj–Ghazvin	112	5.2	581	146	115	139	109	72	—	—
IX Ghazvin–Bandar Pahlavy	204	12.5	2,546	—	—	494	771	861	267	153
X Avadj–Malayer	202	5.2	1,051	241	169	201	227	73	140	—
XI Malayer–Andimeshk	383	7.9	3,016	93	136	546	715	510	470	546
Total (I–XI)	2,387	6.8	16,240	773	1,506	3,507	4,369	4,000	1,390	699
(total cost = 100)			100	5	9	22	27	25	8	4
B. May 1959 estimate of total cost[b]			11,784	911	4,085	5,259	1,530	—	—	—
(total cost = 100)			100	8	35	44	13	—	—	—

[a] See also Table 3; the annual costs are calculated on the basis of the actual construction (contractors') cost data by individual lots and were obtained from the consultants involved in this project, spring 1965. The consultants' costs have been added to the construction costs of each road pro rata. The years refer to normal calendar years.

[b] Cash flow estimates made in 1959; the years in the original estimates are Iranian calendar years running from March 21 to March 20.

Note: For location of the project roads, see Map 2, p. 12.

Sources: A. The consultants, Tehran, 1965.
B. Progress report, October 5, 1959.

77

TABLE 29: Description of the Project Roads before and after Reconstruction and Completion Dates

Road	Length[a] (kms)	Before Reconstruction	After Reconstruction	Completion[b]
I Hamadan–Khosravy	371	poor gravel road	7 meters asphalt; 10% reduction in length (40 kms)	May 1961
II Shahabad–Malavi	158	earth trail	6 meters asphalt	May 1963
III Kermanshah–Saghez	306	Divandareh–Saghez (93 kms) earth road; Kermanshah–Divandareh (213 kms) poor gravel	6 meters gravel	June 1962
IV Divandareh–Bijar	55	earth trail	6 meters gravel	Sept. 1961
V Rudehen–Babol	156	not passable any more; alternatives: via Chaluz or Sari	6.50 meters asphalt; 100 km reduction in length compared with connection via Chaluz	Dec. 1961
VI Khoramshahr–Andimeshk	283	poor gravel	7 meters asphalt	Mar. 1961
VII Ahwaz–Sar Bandar	157	Ahwaz–Gowpai: (47 kms) very poor asphalt; Gowpai–Sar Bandar (110 kms), earth	7 meters asphalt	Sept. 1962
VIII Avadj–Ghazvin	112	poor gravel	7 meters asphalt	Oct. 1960
IX Ghazvin–Bandar Pahlavy	204	poor gravel	7 meters asphalt; 20% reduction in length (50 kms)	Feb. 1963
X Avadj–Malayer	202	good gravel	7 meters asphalt	Oct. 1962
XI Malayer–Andimeshk	383	very poor gravel	7 meters asphalt	Apr. 1963

Note: For location of the project roads, see Map 2.
Source: IBRD Projects Department.

[a] After reconstruction.
[b] The completion date of each road is computed as the average of the completion dates of the individual lots (provided by consultants), weighted by their respective lengths. The completion date of a lot is assumed to be reached when 90 percent of the work on that lot has been completed.

impact of traffic capacity constraints "with" and "without" improvement. The gross benefit (i.e. road user savings) of some of the project roads may, on this account, be somewhat underestimated.

TABLE 30:   Road User Savings by Type of Vehicle and Road Improvement

(rials per km)

		Trucks	
Type of Road	Light Vehicle[a]	Two-axle, 10.5 ton	Three-axle, 15 ton
Savings as a Result of Road Quality Improvements			
From:			
Good gravel to paved	.875	2.315	3.679
Poor gravel[b] to paved	1.361	4.456	7.316
Earth to paved	1.866	6.598	10.952
Earth to good gravel	.991	4.283	7.273
Poor gravel[b] to good gravel	.486	2.141	3.537
Savings as a Result of Reduction in Distance			
Paved	4.600	7.760	9.912
Good gravel[c]	5.475	10.075	13.591
Poor gravel[c]	5.961	12.216	17.228
Earth[c]	6.466	14.358	20.864

[a] Savings of "light vehicles" calculated on the basis of the simple average of the operating costs of the two types of passenger cars used in Iran, (see Table 20, p. 55).

[b] Data for "poor" gravel road calculated on the basis of the simple average of operating costs on "good" gravel and earth roads. The data for "gravel" roads in Table 20 refer to "good" gravel roads.

[c] Based on savings as a result of reduction in distance for paved roads and savings from road quality improvements.

Note: "Very poor" asphalt and "very poor" gravel (see Table 29) have been treated as good gravel and earth respectively.

Source: Chapter VI, Table 20, p. 55, and p. 56.

The *road user savings per vehicle*, due to road quality improvements and shortening of distance, are based on the estimates of Chapter VI. Some adjustments were necessary, however, to relate the savings more closely to the state of the project roads before and after reconstruction. Table 30 classifies the project roads in greater detail than the standard categories of paved, gravel and earth used for the main estimates of road user costs and savings; it also indicates by how many kilometers the length of some roads was reduced. Road user costs for each project road have then been derived by interpolation between the cost of roads of standard quality. The basic road user costs data have further been applied to the vehicle composition on the project roads, given by the traffic counts of 1960–62. The resulting unit road user costs and savings per km, and the additional savings on account of shortening of the roads, if any, are summarized in Table 31. These benefits per vehicle unit and per km are assumed to continue for twenty years, the most reasonable assumption of the life of the project roads. However, the economics of a shorter lifetime of fifteen years has also been studied.

TABLE 31: Unit Cost Savings by Road

(rials per vehicle-km)

Road	Road User Costs Before	Road User Costs After	Year-Round Costs	Road User Savings	Shortening of Road[a]	Total Savings
I	8.089	4.446	10.429	3.643	1.124	4.767
II	10.052	4.523	. .	5.529	—	5.529
III	8.667	6.448	. .	2.219	—	2.219
IV	10.817	6.909	. .	3.908	—	3.908
V	. .	. .	6.237	. .	3.998	3.998
VI	8.385	4.567	. .	3.818	—	3.818
VII	7.888	4.134	. .	3.754	—	3.754
VIII	8.235	4.499	. .	3.736	—	3.736
IX	7.684	4.283	9.990	3.401	2.449	5.850
X	6.881	4.727	. .	2.154	—	2.154
XI	10.012	4.511	. .	5.501	—	5.501

[a] The road user savings per vehicle-km resulting from a reduction in travelling distance have been calculated on the basis of the length of the road *after* reconstruction.
Source: Tables 28, 29, 30 and 15.

Cost-Benefit Comparisons

The cost and benefit streams thus arrived at have been converted into present worth in 1962. A 10 percent interest rate has been used throughout the present worth calculations. The results per km of road are shown graphically in Chart 4. On the whole, as Chart 4 shows, the (discounted) benefits of the project far exceed its (discounted) costs, but the Kermanshah–Saghez and Divandareh–Bijar roads (Roads III and IV) show negative net benefits.

There are considerable differences in (discounted) costs and benefits per km of the various roads, but high costs and high benefits are imperfectly correlated. The very high cost of the mountainous Rudehen–Babol road, for example, is only just compensated by equally high benefits; the very cheap Kermanshah–Saghez and Divandareh–Bijar roads are still uneconomic because of their low benefits (mainly due to low volumes of traffic); but the expensive

80

CHART 4

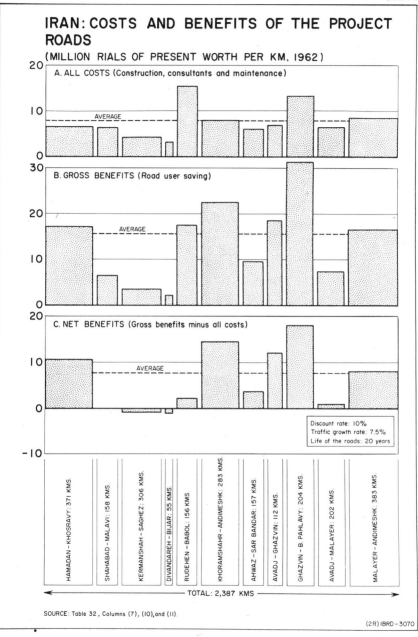

IRAN: COSTS AND BENEFITS OF THE PROJECT ROADS

(MILLION RIALS OF PRESENT WORTH PER KM, 1962)

A. ALL COSTS (Construction, consultants and maintenance)

AVERAGE

B. GROSS BENEFITS (Road user saving)

AVERAGE

C. NET BENEFITS (Gross benefits minus all costs)

AVERAGE

Discount rate: 10%
Traffic growth rate: 7.5%
Life of the roads: 20 years

HAMADAN – KHOSRAVY: 371 KMS.

SHAHABAD – MALAVI: 158 KMS.

KERMANSHAH – SAGHEZ: 306 KMS.

DIVANDAREH – BIJAR: 55 KMS.

RUDEHEN – BABOL: 156 KMS.

KHORAMSHAHR – ANDIMESHK: 283 KMS.

AHWAZ – SAR BANDAR: 157 KMS.

AVADJ – GHAZVIN: 112 KMS.

GHAZVIN – B. PAHLAVY: 204 KMS.

AVADJ – MALAYER: 202 KMS.

MALAYER – ANDIMESHK: 383 KMS.

◄——— TOTAL: 2,387 KMS ———►

SOURCE: Table 32, Columns (7), (10), and (11).

(2R) IBRD – 3070

81

Ghazvin–Bandar Pahlavy and Malayer–Andimeshk roads are excellent investments, given the high benefits of these roads.[2]

Table 32 shows the factors underlying the differences in net benefits. Columns 3 to 6 of the table refer to the base year.

Column 3 of the table shows the ADT (average daily traffic) for each of the roads in the first year that benefits were generated. These traffic data are based on the 1960–62 data (Table 15, p. 43), adjusted to the specific year of completion of each road assuming an annual rate of growth of 7.5 percent. No traffic count information is available for Road II; the figure in brackets [218] is the ADT which would be required in order to break even. The traffic on the various roads ranges from a high of 992 to a low of 87 vehicles per day; as discussed earlier, these figures may well overstate actual levels of inter-city traffic. Savings in distance are important for the Ghazvin–Bandar Pahlavy road, comprising about one-half of the benefits (column 5). For the Rudehen–Babol road all road user savings result from the shortcut provided by the new road, i.e. a 100-km reduction in travelling distance compared with the connection via Chaluz.

Finally, column 7 adjusts the "base year" present worth of the road user savings per km to a common reference year 1962.

The costs of the project roads, in terms of present worth in 1962, are summarized in columns 8, 9 and 10. The bulk of the costs consists of construction and consultants' costs, with maintenance costs adding only a few percent to the total. The range of costs per km, though less than that of benefits, is substantial, reflecting wide differences in standards and terrain.

The net economic results of the roads, per km, are given in columns 11 and 12. Only Roads III and IV show negative results. The percentage difference between benefits and costs are sufficiently large for this conclusion to appear reasonably firm. Their absolute significance appears more clearly from Table 33 which shows the discounted surplus (loss) for the full length of each road section. The "losses" on the Divandareh–Bijar and Kermanshah–Saghez roads (III and IV) are quite small by comparison with the "profits"

---

[2] The very high return on some of the project roads suggests that investments in these roads should have been undertaken earlier.

TABLE 32: Discounted Costs and Benefits of the Project Roads per Kilometer

Road (1)	Length in kms (2)	ADT Base Year [a] (3)	Gross Benefits — Present Value in Base Year · Per Vehicle-km ('000 rials) (4)	[b] (5)	Total (6)	Total (7)	Costs — Present Value in 1962 (million rials per km) · Construction plus Consultants' (8)	Maintenance (9)	Total (10)	Net Benefits (11)	% of Total (12)
I Hamadan–Khosravy	371	554	28.2	6.7	15.62	17.18	6.37	.23	6.60	10.58	160
II Shahabad–Malavi	158	[218][c]	32.8	—	7.12	6.47	6.17	.30	6.47	0	0
III Kermanshah–Saghez	306	262	13.1	—	3.44	3.44	4.06	.09	4.15	—.71	—17
IV Divandareh–Bijar	55	87	23.1	—	2.01	2.21	2.78	.36	3.14	—.93	—30
V Rudehen–Babol	156	743	23.7	23.7	17.61	17.61	14.98	.56	15.54	2.07	13
VI Khoramshahr–Andimeshk	283	903	22.6	—	20.41	22.45	7.81	.26	8.06	14.39	179
VII Ahwaz–Sar Bandar	157	436	22.2	—	9.69	9.69	5.84	.33	6.17	3.52	57
VIII Avadj–Ghazvin	112	700	22.1	—	15.48	18.73	6.49	.28	6.77	11.96	177
IX Ghazvin–Bandar Pahlavy	204	992	34.6	14.5	34.32	31.20	13.12	.14	13.25	17.95	135
X Avadj–Malayer	202	593	12.7	—	7.56	7.56	6.29	.23	6.53	1.03	16
XI Malayer–Andimeshk	383	563	32.6	—	18.33	16.67	8.23	.30	8.53	8.14	95
Average	—	583	23.5	—	14.45	14.67	7.60	.28	7.87	—	—

[a] The base year for each road is the year construction was completed.
[b] These are the road user savings per km resulting from a distance reduction, based on road length after reconstruction.
[c] The ADT which would have been required to break even; no traffic count data are available for this road.

Notes: Cost and benefit data are based on the assumption of a 20-year lifetime of the roads, a 7.5 percent annual traffic growth rate, and a discount rate of 10 percent. For location of the project roads, see Map 2.
Sources: Tables 28, 29, 31 and 15.

TABLE 33: Discounted Net Benefits, Total Road Sections, Present Value in 1962

	Road	Total Costs	Net Benefits (Loss) i.e. Total Benefits minus Total Costs
			[million rials]
I	Hamadan–Khosravy	2,449	3,925
II	Shahabad–Malavi	1,022	0
III	Kermanshah–Saghez	1,270	(−217)
IV	Divandareh–Bijar	173	(−51)
V	Rudehen–Babol	2,424	323
VI	Khoramshahr–Andimeshk	2,281	4,072
VII	Ahwaz–Sar Bandar	969	553
VIII	Avadj–Ghazvin	758	1,340
IX	Ghazvin–Bandar Pahlavy	2,703	3,662
X	Avadj–Malayer	1,319	208
XI	Malayer–Andimeshk	3,267	3,118
	Total, excluding Road II	17,613	16,932
	Total, including Road II	18,635	16,932
		(*US$ million*)	
	Total, excluding Road II	234.8	225.8
	Total, including Road II	248.5	225.8

Source: Table 32, columns 2, 7 and 10.

on the other roads. Khoramshahr–Andimeshk–Malayer, Ghazvin–Bandar Pahlavy, and Hamadan–Khosravy appear the most successful investments.

Alternative Assumptions and Estimates

Because the benefit data leave much to be desired, the authors have considered the effect of alternative assumptions and estimates. First, what happens to net benefits if one assumes lower initial volumes of traffic, or lower unit road user savings per km? If the initial traffic volume, for example, were 25 percent lower, gross benefits would, of course, be correspondingly reduced. This does not essentially alter the profitability of the various road improvements, except for the Avadj–Malayer and Rudehen–Babol roads (X and V). For the Hamadan–Khosravy road (I), in particular, where the traffic count data appeared implausibly high, the initial traffic volume could be more than halved without making the road improvement uneconomic. Lower road user savings give similar results.

Upward changes in initial traffic, or in unit road user costs, would, of course, simply raise the profitability of most of the roads. For the two roads with negative net benefits the upward revision in gross benefits would need to be some 20–40 percent to change the negative result. The authors tend to believe, however, that their initial traffic volumes based on the traffic counts err if anywhere on the high side (see Annex I). The full 20–40 percent upward adjustment would, therefore, have to come from the unit savings, which seems unlikely.

One possible cause of higher unit savings would be, for some roads, if the improvement not only upgraded the pavement, but also eased the gradients and curves. This would increase running speeds and also decrease operating costs. But the effect of higher running speeds on savings appears to be generally rather small, even when the increase in speed is large.[3]

The possible effects of a shorter lifetime of the road and of a lower rate of traffic growth have also been analyzed. A fifteen-year life (instead of twenty years taken in this study)[4] reduces the present worth of gross benefits by about 21 percent; a 5 percent rate of traffic growth (instead of 7.5 percent) reduces it by some 18 percent. If both lifetime of the road and traffic growth rate are reduced, the gross benefits decline by some 32 percent. Costs are hardly affected; a shorter lifetime reduces maintenance costs, with a corresponding reduction in total cost of less than one-half of one percent. On balance, of course, the profitability of all road improvements is reduced. But even with a fifteen-year life and 5 percent traffic growth rate the "profitable" roads continue to show positive net benefits, with the exception again of the Avadj–Malayer and Rudehen–Babol roads.

Finally, it is of some interest to examine to what extent the uneconomic results of the improvement of the Kermanshah–Saghez and Divandareh–Bijar roads are attributable to the rise in construction costs (described in Chapter III). As the figures below illustrate, cost increases of the Kermanshah–Saghez and Divandareh–Bijar roads were much less than the average cost increase of about 40 percent, and even at the original construction costs (ex-

---

[3] QRUS, Table 11, p. 28.
[4] See Annex II, p. 118.

cluding contingency) these roads are hardly economic. Of the two marginal roads, the return on the Rudehen–Babol road suffered from an exceptionally large cost overrun. Even with only an average construction cost performance, this road would have shown substantial positive results; and *a fortiori* at the original construction cost level:

	Road	Benefits less Actual Costs as % of Actual Costs	Percentage Increase in Construction Costs	Benefits less Original Cost Estimates as % of Original[a] Cost Estimates
III	Kermanshah–Saghez	−17	17	− 3
IV	Divandareh–Bijar	−30	18	−17
V	Rudehen–Babol	+13	66	+88
X	Avadj–Malayer	+16	35	+57

[a] Excluding contingency allowance of 10 percent.
Source: Column 1, Table 32, p. 83; column 2, Table 4, p. 23; column 3, cols. 1 and 2.

Alternative Investments

Given these results, the authors also considered whether some alternative road projects or project variants would perhaps have been preferable. The lowering of design standards could have given substantial savings in construction costs as discussed before (see also Chapter IV). Whether this would improve the net benefits would depend, of course, on the corresponding reduction in unit savings that it would entail. For example, lowering the design standards of the Rudehen–Babol road—reducing its width by 50 cm to 6 meters and applying gravel instead of an asphalt surface—would have reduced the cost of this mountain road by only some 10 percent but the gross benefits by over 40 percent. The Kermanshah–Saghez and Divandareh–Bijar roads, which were upgraded to gravel roads 6 meters wide, offer still less scope for lowering design standards. But for the latter small road, simple grading of the existing earth road might possibly have given better results; and improvement of the Divandareh–Saghez earth section alone without the Kermanshah–Divandareh section, which was already in passable condition, might have been economically justified. For the other roads, given the unit road user savings (Table 31) and the typical construction costs (Chapter V), the net benefits would have been adversely affected in all cases if lower design standards or stage construction had been applied.[5]

All roads have been built for a fourteen-ton axle load instead of the eight-ton standard more customary in other countries. The additional construction costs for a fourteen-ton axle load standard appear to be small in Iran, and these additional costs are probably compensated by the general tendency for larger trucks to have lower running costs per ton capacity. It should be noted, however, that the issue concerns not heavier trucks but trucks with heavier axle-loads. The authors have found no evidence in Iran on the relative economics of trucks with different axle-loads.[6] Overloading the capacity of the truck and its engine and/or the weight capacity of the road, a common practice in Iran (at least in the recent past), is presumably uneconomic.

The possibility of alternative railway rehabilitation between the Gulf ports and Tehran, or development of alternative routes for imports through the northern ports and/or through Bandar Abbas should be taken into account in any judgment of the economic

---

[5] This conclusion depends entirely upon the interrelationships between the specific magnitudes of the road user savings and typical construction costs estimated in this study for Iran. To what extent these interrelationships, and consequently the above conclusion, apply also in other countries, is a question which needs further investigation.

[6] See Hewes and Oglesby: *Highway Engineering*, (1954), p. 138: "In many states (of the U.S.A.) the desire of the trucking industry for more economical operation through the use of larger and heavier vehicles has resulted in demands for upward revisions of existing limits (on axle loads). At times legislatures have yielded to these pressures without fully appreciating the results. It must be emphasized that the American Association of State Highway Officials recommendations represent the carefully weighed judgment of engineers from the state highway departments and the Bureau of Public Roads. Upward or downward revision of some of these standards may appear desirable at a later date, but only after the results of current and projected engineering and economic research have been carefully interpreted." In Europe also, in recent years, there has been a tendency to some upward revision in axle-load standards. A recent publication of the International Road Union, *Study and Research on Road Technique and the Economy of Infrastructures*, (Geneva, 1966), quotes data for the U.S.A. and France (pp. 58 and 85) on the impact of changes in axle weights on transport costs:

Country	Increase in axle weight	Decrease in transport cost
U.S.A.	from 8.2 to 10.9 ton	22.0 percent–28.2 percent
France	from 10 to 13 ton	8.5 percent

merits of the project. On balance, such developments are not likely, at least in the more immediate future.

More important for the economics of the 396 km Burujird–Ghazvin section of the project roads is the reconstruction of the Burujird–Qum shortcut from the Trans-Iranian highway to Tehran. As pointed out in Chapter II, completion of the road will enable northbound traffic to cut 180 kms off the route to Tehran. This road appears to be quite justified economically even after the improvement of the route by way of Ghazvin. The improvement on the Burujird–Ghazvin section, therefore, would appear to have been hardly necessary if it is to serve only the small remaining volume of traffic. This would have emerged clearly prior to this investment if such interrelated road projects had been considered jointly. Piecemeal successive analysis can be quite misleading if the same transport flow is used more than once to measure the benefits.

Concluding Remarks

In brief conclusion of the cost-benefit analysis, on the data chosen as a base,[7] it can be said that, in spite of the substantial increase in construction costs, the project as a whole was successful and yielded a satisfactory return. Many uncertainties and qualifications attach to the benefit estimates, but the overall conclusion holds even if the benefits were substantially—say 25 percent—lower. Only two road sections, Kermanshah–Saghez and Divandareh–Bijar, involving rather minor investments, showed a negative result. Two others, Rudehen–Babol and Avadj–Malayer, involving about one-fifth of total costs, appear somewhat marginal and could give negative results if the benefits were substantially overestimated. One of these roads, Avadj–Malayer, as well as the Avadj–Ghazvin section, will probably show negative results after the completion of the Burujird–Qum shortcut to Tehran. The remaining roads appear good investments even within the very wide margins of error that attach to the benefits of some of these roads.

---

[7] Naturally the conclusions of the analysis can only be as good as their data. Annex I contains a more complete discussion of this.

IX

CONCLUSIONS AND RECOMMENDATIONS

In this final chapter, the authors summarize some of the conclusions that have emerged from this study—most of them tentative and/or subject to qualifications. They also make some general recommendations for data collection and analysis.

Conclusions

Construction Cost Increases and Construction Delays

A major reason for the increases in construction costs above the original estimate and for the delays, appears to have been that the preparation did not take sufficient account of all the factors. The serious difficulties of contractors required cancellation of their contracts in some cases; in others, financial help within the legal framework of the contract.

Typical Construction Costs

These costs depend on such factors as terrain conditions, type of surface, width of pavement, etc. For non-mountainous terrain, the type of surface appears to be the most important cost factor; in mountainous terrain, width is most important.

In flat or rolling terrain, a paved road which is one meter wider than a narrower gravel road is about 50 percent more expensive. This significant difference suggests that, for low traffic volumes, lower-standard roads may offer an economic alternative.

Stage Construction

Stage construction, which gears successive road improvements more closely to the development of traffic, is often not considered in practice because the total (undiscounted) costs are much greater than those of single-stage construction. The available data for Iran indicate, however, that *undiscounted* costs may increase only some 5 percent with stage construction.

Maintenance Costs

Maintenance costs per km, for the range of traffic normal for each type of road, rise in Iran with the standard of the road, not so much because of purely routine maintenance (clearing of ditches), but because of the cost of resurfacing every four to five years.

Traffic Data

Traffic count data were the best available source for making projections. A comparison of all available data on the main transport artery northbound from the Gulf between Khoramshahr and Ahwaz suggests that the weighing station data underestimate the actual flow of goods by some 60–75 percent, on the basis of the small sample used in this study. The best estimate of traffic was found to lie between a lower estimate derived from an analysis of "imports minus rail transport" and a higher estimate derived from traffic count data.

The weighing stations provided directly useful information on the structure of transport flows. For traffic to Tehran and beyond, some 70 percent originates in the southern ports (imports), some 10–15 percent in the middle west (the Hamadan/Kermanshah area) and some 15 percent, the remainder, in the northwest (Tabriz/Rezaiyeh). The predominance of imports in the Trans-Iranian highway traffic has implications for the (re)construction of the

Burujird–Qum–Tehran connection undertaken in 1964. After this 180-km shorter road to Tehran is completed, the bulk of the traffic on the Burujird–Ghazvin road is likely to be diverted to the new road.

Diversion from Railways

Rail and road data on the transport of imports from Khoramshahr and Bandar Shahpoor suggest that a shift from rail to road was taking place and had accelerated around 1962, coinciding with the completion of the roads. On balance the authors think that the reconstruction of the Trans-Iranian highway with the corresponding reduction in trucking rates was a major factor in this diversion.

Vehicle Registration, Fuel Consumption and
Future Growth of Traffic

Vehicle registration and fuel consumption data over time give a fair indication of the overall development of traffic. The overall increases in Iran of 10 percent per year conceal widely divergent rates for passenger cars versus trucks, and for gasoline versus diesel oil consumption. On balance, inter-city traffic of passenger cars and light gasoline-fueled trucks may have grown by some 10 percent per year, and of heavier trucks by some 7 percent. These overall data relate to national trends which may or may not be indicative for specific roads. From import projections, an estimate of 7 percent was also obtained for future growth of (truck) traffic on the Trans-Iranian highway. For all traffic on the project roads, an estimate of 7.5 percent growth p.a. was adopted.

Road User Savings and Rate Reductions

Road user costs, referring to running costs at specific speeds on specific types of road, provide a convenient concept for estimating road user savings from improving the quality of roads. On a capacity ton km basis, the authors' estimates of unit road user savings are of the same order of magnitude as those in the original appraisal report. Furthermore, they appear realistic. Available evidence suggests that by 1961 trucking rates had come down by some 20 percent on the Khoramshahr–Tehran route, presumably reflecting the improvement in road conditions. Even fewer data are available on rates on other routes, but average round trip rates between Khoramshahr and Tehran may have fallen by 17–19 percent.

Average Year-Round Trucking Costs and Rates

Information obtained on average year-round trucking costs in Iran, relating to the operation of (a fleet of) vehicles on paved roads, provide a good base for the measurement of savings from a reduction in travelling distance (see Annex II). Year-round trucking costs per vehicle-km are about 60–80 percent higher than the corresponding road user costs derived from "Quantification of Road User Savings." Two-thirds to three-quarters of the difference is explained by differences in concepts: year-round trucking cost figures imply a lower average road speed and higher wage costs and include taxes and overheads. While it is more difficult to reconcile the remaining differences, the authors take the cost figures to be broadly consistent. A comparison of the year-round trucking costs and average trucking rates in Iran suggests that cost and rate figures in the study are also broadly consistent.

Rail and Truck Rates

Allowing for the difference in rail and road distances, the comparable rates between Khoramshahr and Tehran were roughly equal from 1961 to 1966. Due to its service characteristics, truck transport has become more attractive at equal rates per ton than rail transport. In mid-1966 the railways introduced large rate reductions for certain categories of southbound traffic.

Development Benefits

The road project in Iran was expected to have substantial development benefits. Unfortunately, the authors found little clear evidence that such benefits had in fact materialized at the time of the reappraisal. Time series on agricultural production or crop area were not available in sufficient detail to give any impression of the possible impact of the road improvements; the results of visual inspection and interviews were largely negative. Also, little evidence was found that the gap between local market prices in the producing region and those in the central market of Tehran had narrowed. Transport costs in Iran account for only about 5–10 percent of the margin between farm and retail prices, and the marketing of food crops is highly monopolistic. The incentive of lower trucking rates would be small even if they were fully passed on to the farmer or consumer. In general, with strongly monopolistic marketing conditions, few if any development benefits should be expected from road improvements.

Cost-Benefit Analysis

On the basis of the available data, a cost-benefit analysis was made for the various road segments. For the project as a whole, the discounted benefits far exceed the discounted costs (at 10 percent). Both costs and benefits per km vary widely among the various roads. Two roads, the Kermanshah–Saghez and Divandareh–Bijar roads, show a negative net present worth. Both of these roads were cheaply built but are uneconomic because of their low benefits. On the other hand, two expensive roads—Ghazvin–Bandar Pahlavy and Malayer–Andimeshk—are excellent investments because of their high benefits. The very high cost of the Rudehen–Babol road, is only just compensated by correspondingly high benefits.

Sensitivity Analysis

How sensitive are these results to lower initial volumes of traffic, a lower rate of traffic growth, lower unit road user savings per km and a shorter lifetime of the road? The authors' analysis indicates that within the margins given, the only roads sensitive to changes in the estimates were the Avadj–Malayer and Rudehen–Babol roads.

Influence of Increases in Construction Costs

The construction cost increases beyond the original estimates had little impact on the unsatisfactory economic results of the Kermanshah–Saghez and Divandareh–Bijar roads. Even with the original construction cost estimates these roads do not appear economic. But the especially large increase in costs of the Rudehen–Babol road reduced the return on this road to a very modest level. A reduction in construction costs through a lowering of design standards, however, would not have improved the economic results.

Need for Comprehensive Analysis

The Ghazvin–Avadj road and, marginally, the Avadj–Malayer road were shown to give a good economic return. However, completion of the Burujird–Qum shortcut to Tehran is likely to result in diversion of the bulk of the traffic on the Burujird (Malayer)–Ghazvin road to the new road. Clearly, nearly the same total road user savings and better economic results could have been obtained without the investment in the Burujird–Ghazvin improvement. This suggests, more generally, that interrelated road projects should be considered jointly. Piecemeal, successive analyses may be quite misleading as the same transport flow is used more than once.

This also applies to diversion of imports to alternative ports. The economics of the development of the Bandar Abbas port and the Khoramshahr–Tehran route, for example, are interrelated and cannot be treated as separate problems. In comparing the Khoramshahr–Tehran railway and the road connection, and also in considering alternative design standards, all the relevant alternatives need to be included.

Deficiencies of Data

As this study illustrates, economic (re)appraisals are dependent on the data used. The lack of and deficiencies in the data can be attributed largely to an inadequate data collection system. Special efforts at data generation were not made for this study, and as a result the authors have arrived at very tentative answers to questions raised.

Recommendations

The recommendations below, if widely adopted, would minimize the need for special inquiries. They have a general validity beyond the Iranian context.

Data Collection

Better data collection is a prerequisite for better transport planning. As a first step, considerable scope exists for assembling data on traffic and transport flows at small additional effort and cost. At a later stage, this should be supplemented by data on rates and costs. More specifically, the authors recommend the following:

Actual counting of traffic should be done regularly and should be the direct responsibility of the ministry responsible for roads. A breakdown of the total traffic flow into some seven types[1] of vehicles would seem adequate. The location of the traffic count points should be outside the urban traffic sphere. The optimal—in the sense of lowest cost consistent with a fair degree of reliability—sample size of traffic counts should be chosen. The introduction of automatic counts to supplement manual counts should be considered.

Weighing station information should, where available, be collected by the ministry on a regular basis, and analyzed in a statistical center. The general lines are indicated in Annex II of this study.

Vehicle registration data should be collected and analyzed in categories similar to those to be used in traffic counts. The power source (gasoline or diesel oil) should also be identified.

Railway statistics should be collected and analyzed in order to arrive at a clear and detailed traffic flow picture showing volume, composition and direction of traffic.

Import and export statistics should be collected and analyzed by ports of entry, commodity composition, volume and value.

A single statistical agency should coordinate the data to be provided by the roads, railways, police, ports, customs and planning office. Further, unless a planning machinery exists which uses the statistics, the collection process soon deteriorates.

Project Appraisal

Appraisal of a road project should contain, as a minimum, the following information in a more or less standardized form:

a. *Analysis by road section,* not exceeding 100–150 kms and preferably smaller:
  – The nature of the terrain traversed (flat, rolling or mountainous).

---

[1] E.g. (a) passenger cars (Volkswagen type, Mercedes type, other); (b) small trucks; (c) two-axle trucks and tankers (the ten-ton type); (d) three-axle trucks and tankers (the fifteen-ton type); (e) five-axle trucks and trailers (thirty-ton type); (f) buses; (g) other (tractors, etc.).

95

- In some detail the condition of the road before (where applicable) and after (re)construction—including distance reduction, if any.
- The estimated consultants' and construction costs per km; construction costs should be broken down into the following categories: earthworks, sub-base, base, culverts, pavement.
- Quantitative discussion of alternative construction possibilities: (a) other design standards, and (b) stage construction.
- Probable schedule of construction.
- The estimated maintenance costs per km without (where applicable) and with (re)construction.
- The observed traffic density—distinguishing at least two types of vehicle—passenger car and truck—with year of reference, source, location of counting point(s) and method of counting.
- The expected rate of traffic growth with reasons for the choice of this rate.
- The expected lifetime of the roads.
- The amount of road user savings per vehicle-km.
- The results of a net present value calculation or alternatively, the rate of return of the road investment.
- Alternative return calculations on the basis of alternative, more pessimistic assumptions as to relevant variables such as the construction cost of the road, the future growth of traffic, and the amount of road user savings per vehicle.

b. *Analysis by types of road and vehicle* (the same types referred to in the traffic count data):
- The road user costs and savings calculation (per km) in detail, according to cost categories, in terms both of volume and value, and with mention of the sources and/or the assumptions used. Cost categories are: fuel consumption (gasoline or diesel oil); oil consumption; tire wear; maintenance costs; depreciation; interest; driver; overheads.

c. *Analysis of traffic patterns:*
- The actual origin and destination pattern of traffic (road as well as rail) together with the main factors underlying this

pattern, both with reference to the overall traffic and the relative positions of road and rail.

- The shortest feasible traffic routes—based on the origins and destination pattern—as compared with the (travelling) routes actually being taken.
- The future development of the main factors underlying the future traffic patterns.

Follow-Up

The authors further recommend that progress reports[2] on road projects include the following information by road sections identical to the division in the original project appraisal report, as well as for the entire project:

- The progress of the work since its beginning and since the last progress report.
- Comparison of the actual and the original construction schedule, and determination of the delay, if any, with reasons. This comparison could be most informatively presented in chart form.
- Cost increases since the beginning of the work and since the previous progress report, with the underlying reasons and their relative importance.

The final progress report, prepared after the completion of the project, should contain, in addition to the foregoing, an analysis of the cost increases by cost categories.

During the period of project implementation and later, a systematic effort should be made to gather information on the economic results actually obtained from the projects.

Present-day Practice of the Bank

As indicated in the Preface, the art of project appraisal is subject to continuous change. Nearly a decade has elapsed since the original appraisal report of the project discussed in this study was written.

---

[2] For example, the periodic supervision reports made in the Bank after the granting of the loan and until the completion of the project.

97

During this period, more experience has accumulated, concepts have been clarified, and improved analytical tools, some involving computer use, have become available. In a number of respects, therefore, the 1959 appraisal report of the Iranian road project is not representative of 1968 Bank practice.

At present, for instance, the Bank insists on more detailed engineering cost estimates before it approves a project. There is a greater use of consultants. The Bank undertakes separate economic analyses of individual roads, and if necessary, key sections, within each project. Regional or national transport surveys or models are increasingly being used *inter alia* to avoid some of the errors which may follow from appraisal of a project in isolation. For those road projects where the expected agricultural benefits are substantial, the Bank requires reasonably firm agricultural development prospects, and tries to ensure that these prospects are likely to be realized. Finally, more attention is being paid to the vexing problem of data. In the recent past, for instance, a greater number of loan agreements have provided for the costs of equipment and planning necessary to improve traffic data collection.

ANNEX I

ADDITIONAL TRAFFIC INFORMATION AND RELIABILITY OF TRAFFIC DATA

This Annex to Chapter V discusses in somewhat more detail information obtained from the truck weighing stations, the traffic counts of 1960–62 and the import and rail statistics.

Weighing Station Registers

To enforce the axle-load limit of 14 tons for trucks, weighing stations have been operating in Iran since 1960. In case of overloading the trucker has to pay a fine, related to excess weight. At these stations, registers are kept for each truck weighed, specifying:

    a. the type of truck (two-, three- or five-axle);
    b. the axle-loads in tons;
    c. the load carried in tons;
    d. the major commodity carried;
    e. the origin and destination of the truck.

In an attempt to supplement the scarce statistics on road transport in Iran, the authors asked the Ministry of Roads to collect, on a sample basis, some data from the books kept by the weighing stations. The data were collected from five weighing stations for one whole day of every month in the years 1961–1964.[1] This material, involving some 6,000 trucks, was subsequently computerized for each weighing station to determine traffic flows. For analytical purposes, the origins and destinations were classified into 10 groups with 21 subdivisions and the commodities into 15 groups with 20 subdivisions.

Traffic flows were constructed by determining the most likely route of travel between the various origins and destinations for trucks passing and registered at a weighing station. This provided useful information on the volume and direction of heavy transport on the roads immediately beyond the weighing stations. Light vehicles and obviously empty trucks are, of course, not covered by the weighing station data, and are excluded throughout the following discussion. Because a great number of trucks go southward empty, the data are useful principally for northbound traffic. For example, observation at the Ahwaz weighing station might be expected to give reliable indications of northbound heavy truck traffic on the Ahwaz–Malavi road section; all such trucks with origin in Ahwaz or before, i.e. Khoramshahr (Abadan) or Bandar Shahpoor, and destination Malavi or beyond, might be expected to pass the Ahwaz weighing station. Observation at Ahwaz might also give reasonable coverage of northbound heavy traffic at Ahwaz, although traffic remaining at Ahwaz would escape notice since the weighing station is located north of the city. As distance increases beyond the weighing station, of course, the data become more and more incomplete as traffic originating beyond or bypassing the weighing station is omitted.

This deficiency could be overcome, in principle, by integrating data from successive weighing stations. This would provide additional coverage for the roads far beyond the "first" weighing station. It also should give some check on the quality of the data on particular road segments, as traffic observations at two or more stations for the same origin and destination should be consistent. Unfortunately, after thorough consideration of the information obtained from the weighing stations at Kermanshah, Dorud, and

---

[1] The stations were at Ahwaz, Kermanshah, Hamadan, Ghazvin and the vicinity of Dorud; data for Dorud covered 1964 only.

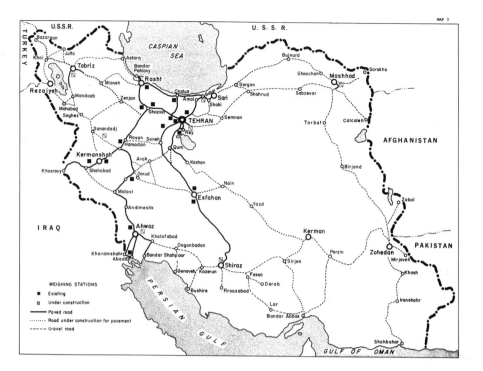

Hamadan these data had to be rejected in view of their many implausibilities.[2] Thus it proved impossible to obtain any close integration of data of successive weighing stations. The following analysis is therefore based only on the data from the Ahwaz and Ghazvin stations.

Annex Table 1 presents a summary of the major characteristics of the loaded truck traffic recorded in the Ahwaz weighing station (light vehicles and empty trucks are *not* recorded). The table distinguishes between several road segments adjoining the weighing

---

[2] For example, traffic data of the Kermanshah weighing station differ widely from those of the Hamadan station for the Kermanshah-Hamadan road, not only for the volume of traffic but also for the composition of trucks and commodities and for the origins and destinations; the same, but to a larger extent still, holds true if information from the two stations for the same day (e.g. April 4, 1964) is compared. Similar results are reached if the data from the Dorud and Hamadan stations are compared with those from the Ghazvin and Ahwaz stations. Of course, no precise correspondence among the data from various weighing stations may be expected because of probable inaccuracies and/or incompleteness in recording and also because only a small sample of the data was collected.

101

ANNEX TABLE 1: North and Southbound Truck Traffic on the Roads Adjacent to Ahwaz, 1961 and 1964

	Khoramshahr–Ahwaz				Bandar Shahpoor–Ahwaz		Ahwaz–Malavi			
	Northbound		Southbound		Northbound		Northbound		Southbound	
	1961	1964	1961	1964	1961	1964	1961	1964	1961	1964
Number of trucks per day,	39	44	17	—	—	14	44	65	25	—
of which two-axle	9	13	4	—	—	6	10	23	6	—
three-axle	27	25	12	—	—	8	31	36	17	—
five-axle	3	5	1	—	—	..	3	6	2	—
Average load per truck (*tons*),	15.6	15.5	14.4	—	—	13.9	15.4	14.8	14.7	—
of which two-axle	11.3	11.0	10.8	—	—	11.2	11.3	11.0	10.8	—
three-axle	15.5	15.0	14.8	—	—	15.4	15.6	15.1	15.1	—
five-axle	29.3	28.6	26.1	—	—	23.4	29.1	28.1	27.1	—
Average distance travelled per truck (*kms*)	1,106	1,100	969	—	—	1,136	1,098	1,097	958	—
of which two-axle	1,126	1,102	1,021	—	—	1,127	1,116	1,080	990	—
three-axle	1,112	1,094	976	—	—	1,147	1,091	1,101	964	—
five-axle	1,047	1,111	818	—	—	1,112	1,110	1,109	866	—
Annual flow of freight[a] (*'000 tons*)	220.9	249.0	84.4	[8.4]	[4.7]	72.6	248.2	352.9	132.3	[4.2]

[a] Sample data multiplied by $\frac{365}{11}$ (in 1961) or $\frac{365}{12}$ (in 1964).

— Data omitted because number of observations is either very small or nil.

Notes: Negligible or nil traffic was recorded southbound from Ahwaz to Bandar Shahpoor. Data on number of trucks and average load are rounded.

Source: Ahwaz weighing station information; data for 1961 based on a sample of 11 days, data for 1964 based on a sample of 12 days: data supplied by the Ministry of Roads.

station, and focuses on the volume of traffic and freight, the types of truck, the average load and average distance travelled by type of truck, and distinguishes between north and southbound traffic.

The most common type of truck is the three-axle truck, followed by the two-axle truck. The average load carried by the recorded trucks varies little between road segments, year, and direction of traffic; two-axle trucks carry around 11 tons, three-axle trucks around 15 tons, and five-axle trucks around 28 tons. The average load carried by all recorded trucks combined is around 15 tons.[3] The average length of the northbound haul, 1,100 kms, differs little among types of truck; 1,109 kms is the distance between the principal origin (Khoramshahr) and destination (Tehran). For southbound traffic the data indicate a somewhat lower average length of haul, 958 kms. Only some 25 percent or less of southbound traffic originates in Tehran[4] and nearly half in the Khoramabad and Yazd/Esfahan regions.

The northbound flow is clearly much more important than the southbound. In 1961, the figures show northbound traffic to be twice or three times as large. For 1964, however, they show hardly any southbound transport at all, which seems unlikely. A possible explanation may be that in 1964 the weighing stations no longer registered southbound traffic. On the other hand, the relative southbound traffic in 1961 may have been somewhat inflated by the large movement of building materials for the building boom in Iran which subsequently subsided.

The Traffic Flow between Khoramshahr and Tehran

The material from the Ghazvin and Ahwaz stations has been combined into an overall picture of the northbound traffic flow on the main traffic artery in Iran, from Khoramshahr and Bandar Shahpoor via Hamadan and Ghazvin to Tehran. Chart 5 shows the relative importance of various origins, destinations, transport volumes and commodities on different sections of this route. Of course, as only a few weighing stations were sampled for this study, other

---

[3] This, of course, does not mean the average load of all trucks travelling, but only of all the heavily laden trucks registered by the weighing stations.

[4] 24 percent of the traffic flow Malavi-Ahwaz and some 15 percent of the flow Ahwaz-Khoramshahr.

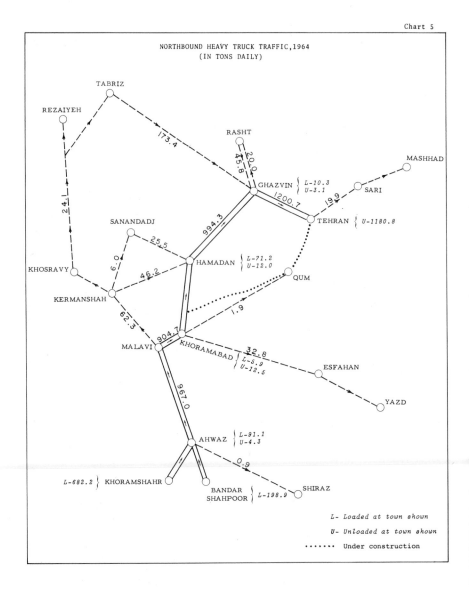

Chart 5

NORTHBOUND HEAVY TRUCK TRAFFIC,1964
(IN TONS DAILY)

roads could be covered only very partially, if at all. Even for the main Khoramshahr–Tehran road, the middle sections between Malavi and Hamadan are inadequately covered because, as explained above, data from intermediate weighing stations between Ahwaz and Ghazvin had to be rejected.

In integrating the data from the two stations, care was taken to avoid double counting: all traffic originating in Khoramshahr, Bandar Shahpoor and Ahwaz was eliminated from the Ghazvin station data. The results are shown in Annex Table 2 and in the flow diagram, Chart 5. A flow diagram was also drawn for 1961. Here we use the 1964 data for northbound traffic, not only because it is the most recent, but also because the Ghazvin and Ahwaz basic data seem more consistent.

As the chart and table indicate, the bulk of the northbound traffic originates in Khoramshahr and is joined in Ahwaz by the flow from Bandar Shahpoor. From Ahwaz on, the traffic volume changes little until Ghazvin—with some traffic leaving the Trans-Iranian highway and some traffic joining it. In Ghazvin the flow from the southern ports is joined by the flow from the northwest (Rezaiyeh and Tabriz), and thus swollen it proceeds to Tehran. Of this traffic to Tehran and hinterland (Sari/Mashhad) some 70 percent originates in the southern ports (imports), some 10–15 percent in the Hamadan/Kermanshah area (the middle west), and the remaining 15 percent in the northwest (Tabriz/Rezaiyeh).

As for the (much smaller) southbound flow of heavy truck transport on the Trans-Iranian highway, the only significant information is provided by the Ahwaz weighing station data for 1961:

Origin	Flow Malavi–Ahwaz	Flow Ahwaz–Khoramshahr	Major Products
	(% of tonnage)	(% of tonnage)	
Tehran	24	15	Various products
Tabriz/Rezaiyeh	12	20	Mainly vegetables/fruits
Khoramabad	16	20	Mainly building materials
Yazd/Esfahan	23	25	About 50% building materials
Other origins	25	20	Various products

As the table shows, the origin and destination of the traffic flows on the Malavi–Ahwaz and Ahwaz–Khoramshahr roads are somewhat different, mainly because a large share of the Tehran trucks were bound for Ahwaz with local consumer goods whereas the trucks from Tabriz/Rezaiyeh are bound for the port.

The analysis of the traffic flows on the Trans-Iranian highway has interesting implications in the light of the (re)construction of the road Burujird–Arak–Qum (232 kms) which is now being undertaken. The project appraisal report for this road (1964) observes:

ANNEX TABLE 2: Northbound Flow of Freight on the Trans-Iranian Highway, 1964

(daily average in tons)

Origin and Destination	Volume	Khoramshahr/Bandar Shahpoor–Ahwaz = 100	Commodity Composition				Iron and Iron-ware	Equipment, Paper, Oil, Textiles	Building Materials	Miscellaneous
			Food Products							
			Wheat	Other cereals	Other food products	Total				
Loaded at Khoramshahr (+)	682.2	—	18.9	10.3	112.2	141.4	113.3	65.8	6.5	355.2
Loaded at Bandar Shahpoor (+)	198.9	—	53.4	1.9	19.5	74.8	9.5	18.8	1.7	94.1
Flow: Khoramshahr/Bandar Shahpoor–Ahwaz	881.1	100	72.3	12.2	131.7	216.2	122.8	84.6	8.2	449.3
Loaded at Ahwaz (+)	91.1	—	23.1	3.2	15.1	41.4	2.7	4.7	0.9	41.4
Unloaded at Ahwaz (−)	5.2	—	1.2			1.2	0.9			3.1
Flow: Ahwaz–Malavi	967.0	109.7	94.2	15.4	146.8	256.4	124.6	89.3	9.1	487.6
To Kermanshah/Khosravy (−)	32.3	—	17.4		7.5	24.9		2.2		5.2
To Sanandadj (−)	6.0	—	1.0			1.0	3.7			1.3
To Rezaiyeh/Tabriz (−)	24.0	—	3.4		9.9	13.3	5.9	1.3		3.5
Flow: Malavi–Khoramabad	904.7	102.7	72.4	15.4	129.4	217.2	115.0	85.8	9.1	477.6
Loaded at Khoramabad (+)	5.9	—	1.3			1.3	2.6			2.0
Unloaded at Khoramabad (−)	12.5	—	4.4		2.7	7.1	2.4			3.0
To Esfahan/Yazd/Qum (−)	34.7	—	3.9		8.1	12.0	3.5	4.7		14.5
Flow: Khoramabad–Hamadan	863.4	98.0	65.4	15.4	118.6	199.4	111.7	81.1	9.1	462.2
Loaded at Hamadan (+)	71.2	—	49.4	6.2	3.6	59.2		0.9	1.3	9.8
Unloaded at Hamadan (−)	12.0	—	5.8		3.7	9.5		1.3		1.2
From Sanandadj (+)	25.5	—	22.3			22.3		1.3		1.9
From Kermanshah/Khosravy (+)	46.2	—	35.3	3.5	0.9	39.7		1.3		5.2
Flow: Hamadan–Ghazvin	994.3	112.8	166.6	25.1	119.4	311.1	111.7	83.3	10.4	477.8
Loaded at Ghazvin (+)	10.3	—	2.3			2.3			1.8	6.2
Unloaded at Ghazvin (−)	3.1	—			3.1	3.1				
From Razaiyeh/Tabriz (+)	173.4	—	8.8	6.7	56.1	71.6		4.6	5.3	91.9
From Rasht (+)	45.8	—	13.5		0.8	14.3	7.8	3.6	10.7	9.4
To Rasht (−)	20.0	—	1.2		1.0	2.2		1.7	0.8	15.3
Flow: Ghazvin–Tehran	1,120.7	136.3	190.0	31.8	172.2	394.0	119.5	89.8	27.4	570.0
Unloaded at Tehran (−)	1,100.8	134.0	175.6	31.8	170.2	377.6	118.2	88.9	27.4	568.7
To Sari/Mashhad (−)	19.9	2.3	14.4		2.0	16.4	1.3	0.9		1.3

"Currently, the north-south artery traffic moves through a round-about highway through Ghazvin and Hamadan, which is about 180 kms longer." As Chart 5 indicates, over 95 percent of the north-bound heavy truck traffic on the road from Hamadan to Ghazvin is destined for Tehran. A very large part of the existing traffic on the Hamadan–Ghazvin road would therefore be attracted by the much shorter Burujird–Qum–Tehran connection. It is not only the traffic originating south of Hamadan which would benefit from the reduction in distance. Some of the traffic which joins the north-bound flow to Tehran in Hamadan (originating in Hamadan itself or in Kermanshah or Sanandaj) would also use the road connection Burujird–Qum–Tehran because the distance Hamadan–Burujird–Tehran is 32 kms less than via Ghazvin.

Commodity Composition

The analysis of the commodity composition of transport as recorded by the weighing stations, is seriously handicapped by the large "miscellaneous" item which, for northbound traffic, constitutes some 50 percent of the total. Of the remainder, food products tend to be most important (some 30 percent), followed by iron and

ANNEX TABLE 3:   Composition of Transport Flow, 1964

	Khoramshahr/ Bandar Shahpoor–Ahwaz		Ahwaz– Malavi		Hamadan– Ghazvin		Ghazvin– Tehran	
	tons per day	% of total	tons per day	% of total	tons per day	% of total	tons per day	% of total
Wheat	72.3	(8)	94.2	(10)	166.6	(17)	190.0	(16)
Other cereals	12.2	(1)	15.4	(2)	25.1	(3)	31.8	(3)
Other food products	131.7	(15)	146.8	(15)	119.4	(12)	172.2	(14)
Total food products	216.2	(25)	256.4	(27)	311.1	(31)	394.0	(33)
Iron & ironware	122.8	(14)	124.6	(13)	111.7	(11)	119.5	(10)
Equipment, paper, oil, textiles	84.6	(10)	89.3	(9)	83.3	(8)	89.8	(7)
Building materials	8.2	(1)	9.1	(1)	10.4	(1)	27.4	(3)
Miscellaneous	449.3	(51)	487.6	(50)	477.8	(48)	570.0	(47)
Grand Total	881.1	(100)	967.0	(100)	994.3	(100)	1,200.7	(100)

ironware and various industrial goods such as equipment, paper, oil and textiles. For southbound traffic, the "miscellaneous" item is less important and amounts to around 20 percent; the rest consists largely of building materials and food products in about equal proportions, at least in 1961; significant 1964 data are not available.

The commodity composition of the northbound traffic flow undergoes, of course, some change on the way to Tehran as Annex Table 3 shows.

In 1961 only 3 percent of wheat carried originated from Khoramshahr/Bandar Shahpoor (imports). In 1964, a poor wheat year in Iran, 35 percent came from the ports and the flow nearly trebled as the traffic flow approached Tehran. Of the inland production areas, the Middle West accounted for about 60 percent and the Ahwaz and Northwest regions for about 20 percent each. If the flow of wheat is excluded from the 1961 and 1964 northbound traffic flows, they become much more similar in structure.

Northbound Heavy Truck Traffic, 1961 and 1964

	1961		1964		
	tons per day	*Khoramshahr/ Bandar Shahpoor– Ahwaz = 100*	*tons per day*	*Khoramshahr/ Bandar Shahpoor– Ahwaz = 100*	*1961 = 100*
Including wheat					
Khoramshahr/Bandar Shahpoor–Ahwaz	618	100	881	100	143
Ahwaz–Malavi	680	110	967	110	142
Hamadan–Ghazvin	792	128	994	113	126
Ghazvin–Tehran	935	151	1,201	136	129
Excluding wheat					
Khoramshahr/Bandar Shahpoor–Ahwaz	614	100	809	100	132
Ahwaz–Malavi	671	109	873	108	130
Hamadan–Ghazvin	650	106	828	102	127
Ghazvin–Tehran	689	128	1,011	125	128

Consistency and Reliability of Weighing-Station, Traffic Count, and Imports-less-Rail Freight Data

As a rough check on the reliability of all three data, the northbound traffic originating in Khoramshahr according to the weighing station data may be compared with estimates derived from import data and from the 1960–62 traffic counts. Assuming that the bulk of the northbound freight from Khoramshahr consists of imports—which can be transported either by rail or by road—the "apparent" volume of road transport can be estimated by deducting the volume of rail freight leaving Khoramshahr from total imports arriving in Khoramshahr. This apparent road transport volume can then be compared with that derived from the Ahwaz weighing station data. Second, the number and composition of trucks going north according to the weighing station may be compared with the traffic count data. As the traffic counts reflect two-way traffic, they need adjustment to a "northbound only" basis. To this end, the original figures have been divided by two on the assumption that triangular trips are insignificant. The resulting traffic volume has been converted into tons carried on the basis of a 100 percent load factor, as northbound trucks tend to be fully loaded. Annex Table 4 presents these two comparisons.

The three measures of the flow of transport from Khoramshahr up north differ widely: the weighing station data suggest by far the lowest volume of transport, the volume derived from the traffic counts is some seven times as high, and the estimate based on imports/rail statistics is roughly in the middle. There are several possible explanations for these very large differences.

The weighing station information may underestimate the actual flow of goods transported over the road because: (a) perhaps not all loaded trucks are weighed; (b) perhaps not all trucks which are weighed are registered; (c) perhaps the sample is not representative and the average sample day is not an average day (see below); and (d) part of the flow of goods is carried by small trucks not registered in the weighing stations.

The imports-less-rail-freight calculation may under- or overestimate the actual flow because: (a) some of the imports stay in the immediate vicinity of the port (e.g., equipment for oil complex in Abadan); (b) in addition to the flow of imports, other goods originating in the port town may swell the transport flow; and (c) the underlying basic data on imports and volume loaded by the railways may be inaccurate.

The traffic counts presumably tend to overestimate the actual flow of transported goods because of the close proximity of the counting stations to the major towns. Furthermore, the assumption

ANNEX TABLE 4: Alternative Estimates of the Volume of Transport from Khoramshahr Northbound, 1961 and 1964

| | 1961 | | Traffic Counts 1960–62 | | | 1964 | |
Estimates derived from:	Imports less Rail Freight	Weighing Station	Khoramshahr	Ahwaz	Average	Weighing Station	Imports less Rail Freight
Annual Volume ('000 tons)	552	221	964[b]	1,391[b]	1,177	249	907
Imports less Rail Freight = 100	100	40	174	252	213	27	100
Average Daily Traffic, Trucks,	[101][a]	39	206	291	249	..	..
of which two-axle		9	105	180	143	..	..
three-axle		27	96	88	92		
five-axle		3	5	23	14		

[a] Based on average truckload of 15 tons.
[b] Based on average truckloads as follows:
two-axle trucks, 10 tons
three-axle trucks, 15 tons
five-axle trucks, 30 tons.

Note: For 1964 no traffic counts are available.
Sources: Table 16, p. 46; Annex Table 1; for traffic count information, Ministry of Roads, Tehran.

110

of an average load factor of 100 percent—used in converting number
of trucks into volume of transport—probably also somewhat over-
states the actual volume of transport. Generally, the quality of the
traffic count data leaves much to be desired (see Chapter V). Either
point, or both points, are illustrated by the traffic count data from
the counting stations just north of Khoramshahr and just south of
Ahwaz, both on the Khoramshahr–Ahwaz road. Not only the level
of the truck traffic but also the composition differs in these two
counts:

Counting Station	Total Truck Traffic	Traffic Composition		
		Two-axle	Three-axle	Five-axle
	(Khoramshahr = 100)	*(total truck traffic = 100)*		
North of Khoramshahr	100	51	47	2
South of Ahwaz	141	62	30	8

Source: See Annex Table 4.

If the locations of the counting stations were well chosen and the
actual counts accurate, one would expect a smaller discrepancy
between the two sets of information.

The basic data underlying the imports-less-rail-freight estimates
of the volume of freight are probably the most reliable, although
customs data for 1964 are reported to have underestimated the
volume of wheat imports. Furthermore, it is not clear whether, and
to what extent, the volume of imports remaining in Khoramshahr/
Abadan is more than offset by the additional volume of traffic
generated in the neighborhood. On balance, the most reasonable
conclusion would seem to be that the true volume of transport lies
somewhere in between the rough "imports minus rail transport"
estimate and that derived from the traffic counts. This would imply
that the transport information derived from the weighing station
data underestimates the actual flow of goods by some 60–75 percent
and cannot be used as an indicator of the *level* of transport.

Sampling Requirements

How far does the size of the sample affect reliability? The foregoing analysis is based on a small sample of 12 whole days in 1964.
Let us take the northbound volume of freight, in tons, from Ahwaz

to Malavi, as registered in the weighing station at Ahwaz. Assume the sample is a simple random sample from a finite population of 365 days. The table below then shows the confidence level and allowable error, by sampling days.[5] A sample size of 12 days implies that in 68 cases out of 100 (confidence level of 68 percent), the sample mean does not deviate more than ±5 percent from the actual figure which would have been found had a complete count been taken. Alternatively it gives a confidence level of 95 percent that error will be rather under 20 percent. The sample should preferably comprise some 33 days to give reliable results—an allowable error of less than 10 percent with a confidence level of more than 95 percent.

Number of Days Required for Sample Giving

Confidence Level	Allowable Error		
	±5%	±10%	±20%
(percent)		*(days)*	
99	148	53	15
95	103	33	9
85	64	18	5
80	54	15	4
68	15	9	2

---

[5] See George W. Snedecor, *Statistical Methods*, Fifth Edition, Iowa State College Press, p. 501.

ANNEX II

ROAD USER SAVINGS AND
YEAR-ROUND COSTS

This Annex to Chapter VI presents in detail the method of calculation, the sources and the assumptions used in arriving at the
road user costs and savings by type of vehicle and road improvement. In addition, it gives detailed information on the typical
trucking costs of a medium-sized trucking firm with 50 trucks
mainly operating on well-maintained paved highways in Iran. The
Annex concludes with a comparison of the road user savings with
the trucking costs and an analysis of the relationship between
trucking costs and rates.

Road User Costs and Savings

The analysis is based on the data in Quantification of Road User
Savings (World Bank Staff Occasional Papers Number 2) which we
shall call QRUS. As in that study, three classes of road are distin-
guished: paved, gravel and earth roads, all in good condition. Road
user costs for these roads of four types of vehicle are calculated for
each class of road (Annex Table 5). These four types are Volkswagen
Sedan 1200 and Mercedes SL-190 (passenger cars, using gasoline)

ANNEX TABLE 5: Road User Costs and Savings, excluding Taxes, per Vehicle by Road Surface, Iran, 1965:

(rials per 1,000 kms)

	Passenger Cars						Trucks					
	Small (Volkswagen)			Big (Mercedes)			Two-axle, 10.5 ton			Three-axle, 15 ton		
Road type:	Paved	Gravel	Earth	Paved	Gravel	Earth	Paved	Gravel	Earth	Paved	Gravel	Earth
Speed (km.p.h.):	80	64	56	80	64	56	72	56	48	72	56	48
Road user costs per vehicle												
Fuel	177	190	214	309	337	383	538	704	915	623	817	1,060
Engine oil	7	9	11	21	26	31	30	43	60	34	48	68
Tire wear	105	210	369	140	280	490	740	1,480	3,320	1,476	2,952	6,643
Depreciation	442	585	806	867	1,148	1,581	464	696	1,160	787	1,181	1,968
Interest	273	338	390	536	663	765	426	545	639	722	924	1,083
Maintenance (parts)	143	195	247	281	357	485	1,022	1,534	2,556	1,733	2,599	4,332
Maintenance (labor)	66	86	119	66	86	119	376	564	940	376	564	940
Driver, assistant, passengers	1,350	1,887	1,928	1,350	1,887	1,928	1,208	1,553	1,812	1,208	1,553	1,812
Total	2,563	3,500	4,084	3,570	4,784	5,782	4,804	7,119	11,402	6,959	10,638	17,906

Road user savings	(rials per km)	(% of road user costs)		(rials per km)	(% of road user costs)		(rials per km)	(% of road user costs)		(rials per km)	(% of road user costs)	
Per vehicle												
Road improvement												
from gravel to paved	.737	22		1.017	22		2.315	33		3.679	35	
earth to gravel	.784	19		1.199	21		4.283	38		7.273	41	
earth to paved	1.521	37		2.212	38		6.598	58		10.952	61	
Per ton capacity												
Road improvement												
from gravel to paved							.220			.245		
earth to gravel							.408			.485		
earth to paved							.628			.730		

Source: See Annex II, pp. 115–121.

114

a two-axle, six-wheel 10.5 ton truck and a three-axle, ten-wheel, 15 ton truck, both using diesel oil. So we can compute the savings for each vehicle-type from an improvement of a given road from gravel to paved, earth to gravel and earth to paved, (bottom of Annex Table 5). Then all we need is the traffic population on the project roads by vehicle-type, and we have the road user savings of the project (Table 20, p. 55).

As Annex Table 5 shows, the road user costs increase with the size of the vehicle and decrease with the quality of the road. The road user savings expressed as a percentage of the operating costs increase with the size of the vehicle and are considerably higher for trucks than for cars.

Annex Table 6 presents the unit prices for each of the cost items used in the road user cost calculation. Prices refer to Iran, in 1960 and 1965, including and excluding taxes, levies, duties, etc. For comparison, the "indicative" unit prices and values taken from QRUS (i.e. without taxes, etc.) are added in a last column.

The gasoline price excluding taxes for 1965 refers to 1964. In 1965, the gasoline retail price was raised by the National Iranian Oil Company to 8 rials per liter without a corresponding tax increase. The 1964 price seems, therefore, a better basis for the calculation of the road user savings. Price changes (excluding taxes, etc.) for passenger cars, trucks and tires have not been significant since 1960, according to our information; 1960 prices have therefore been assumed the same as 1965 prices. Somewhat conflicting information was received concerning the development of labor costs in Iran since 1960. On the basis of available wage statistics in Iran and corroborating evidence (slow economic growth and a fairly constant price level over the five years, an annual increase of less than two percent in the cost of living index) the wage level has been assumed stable.

The Iranian 1965 prices, excluding taxes, are slightly higher than the prices used in QRUS for all items, except gasoline, and considerably higher for wages.

Fuel Consumption

The Volkswagen and Mercedes used in this study correspond with the Volkswagen and "American" car used in QRUS. Prices are taken before tax. It was necessary to allow for the fact that the

ANNEX TABLE 6: Prices, 1965 and 1960, including and excluding Taxes

(rials)

	1965 excluding taxes	1965 including taxes	1960 including taxes	1964/65 QRUS "indicative" prices and values[e]
Fuel and oil (liters)				
Diesel oil	2.25	2.50	2.25	2.5
Gasoline	2.65[a]	5.00	4.50	3.53
Engine oil[b]	14.20	18.00	18.00	14.18
Vehicles (excluding tires)				
Passenger car, small[c]	130,000	212,000	212,000	108,700
Passenger car, big[c]	225,000	430,000	430,000	217,400
Two-axle truck (10.5 ton)[d]	852,000	1,150,000	979,800	789,200
Three-axle truck (15.0 ton)[d]	1,444,000	1,950,000	1,660,600	1,293,200
Tires				
Tire, passenger car, small	1,500	1,500	1,500	1,250
Tire, passenger car, big	2,000	2,000	2,000	1,630
Tire, two-axle truck, 11 x 24	10,000	10,000	10,000	9,290
Tire, three-axle truck, 12 x 24	12,000	12,000	12,000	9,290
Labor (hours)				
Driver (passenger)	60	60	60	18.75
Assistant	27	27	27	—
Maintenance labor	100	100	100	30.00

a Refers to 1964 (see p. 117).
b Price of engine oil has fluctuated over time; the tax component of 3.80 rials per liter is based on an estimate.
c Volkswagen Sedan 1200 and Mercedes SL 190 respectively.
d Mack trucks.
e Truck prices calculated on the basis of straight line interpolation (taking into consideration the net weight of the vehicles) between trucks III and IV of QRUS. Tire prices for trucks refer to size 11 x 22.5.

Sources: Ministry of Finance, National Iranian Oil Company, Mercedes importer, Mack importer, B. F. Goodrich Iran SA, Iran Gaz, all in Tehran, and various trucking firms in Tehran and Khoramshahr; for last column, see QRUS, Table 10, p. 25.

Iranian trucks have a life of 20 years against 7 years in QRUS, and use diesel oil instead of gasoline. The basis for this calculation was Truck III in QRUS, with a gross vehicle weight of 25.9 tons. The diesel oil/gasoline consumption ratio for a truck of this weight is 10:14.[1] This ratio was used to estimate the diesel oil consumption of the Iranian trucks (18.5 tons and 27 tons), on paved roads, in liters per km.

Fuel consumption of Truck III on gravel roads is 131 percent of its consumption on paved roads at the respective "bench mark" speed. On earth roads it is 170 percent.[2] These ratios were applied to the fuel consumption of the Iranian trucks on gravel and paved roads.

Engine Oil Consumption

Engine oil consumption is a minor item in vehicle operating costs. For the trucks in Iran it was calculated on the basis of the information for Trucks II and III of QRUS. The interpolation was based on the load capacity of the trucks.

Engine Oil Consumption of Trucks

(liters per 1,000 kms)

	Truck Types			
	II	Two-axle	Three-axle	III
Load Capacity (tons)	3.52	10.50	15.00	15.06
Engine oil consumption[a]				
paved roads	1.6	2.1	2.4	2.4
gravel roads	2.3	3.0	3.4	3.4
earth roads	3.3	4.2	4.8	4.8

[a] The three-axle truck is assumed to equal III; the two-axle truck is calculated on the basis of interpolation between II and III (load capacity used as basis for interpolation).

Tire Wear

The tire wear calculation for the three-axle truck is based on the data for Truck III of QRUS[3] whereas the tire wear for the two-axle

---

[1] *Supplementary Report of the Highway Cost Allocation Study*, U.S. Congress, House Document No. 124, (Washington, D.C., 1965), p. 306.

[2] QRUS, Table 11, variant B, p. 29.

[3] It is here assumed that the effect on the tire wear of the greater number of wheels of Truck III of QRUS, i.e. 14, as compared with 10 for the three-axle truck, is offset by the correspondingly lower wheel load.

truck is derived from the tire wear of the three-axle truck on the basis of their respective number of tires.

Tire Wear of Trucks

(as percentage of wear of 1 tire per 1,000 kms)

	Truck Types	
	Two-axle	Three-axle
Number of wheels	6	10
On paved road	7.4	12.3
On gravel road	14.8	24.6
On earth road	33.2	55.4

Depreciation

The average life of trucks in Iran is twenty years, while that for the larger trucks (III and IV) in QRUS is seven years. Depreciation of trucks on paved roads has been calculated in this study on the basis of Iranian data on vehicle lifetime and annual mileage, using the general method for calculating depreciation outlined in QRUS.[4] Taking into account the specific speed of trucks on paved roads (72 kms p.h.) and the conversion factors for depreciation on gravel and earth roads given in QRUS,[5] the depreciation for the trucks on different types of road can be calculated.

Depreciation of Trucks

(per 1,000 kms)

(as percentage of the depreciable value of the vehicle)

Paved roads	0.05450
Gravel roads	0.08175
Earth roads	0.13625

Interest Costs

As in QRUS, these were calculated on the basis of 10 percent p.a. of half the depreciable value of the truck. Taking into account the

---

[4] QRUS, p. 61, footnote 9; for year-round average road speeds of trucks see p. 60, para. 38. The average annual mileage of the Iranian trucks is 75,000 kms. The general formula for lifetime of the truck of 20 years is given below:

$$d \text{ (20 years lifetime)} = \frac{1}{18.52\ s + 500},$$

where d is depreciation per 1,000 kms expressed as a percentage of the depreciable value of the vehicle, and s is specific speed in kms per hour (72 kms p.h.).

[5] QRUS, p. 69, para. 51 and following, especially Annex Table 21.

relationship between annual mileage and year-round average road speed,[6] the amount of interest per 1,000 kms for both trucks is shown below.

Interest Costs of Trucks

(per 1,000 kms)

Speed *(km per hour)*	*(as percentage of depreciable value of the vehicle)*
72 (paved road)	.050
56 (gravel road)	.064
48 (earth road)	.075

Maintenance Costs: Parts and Labor

A distinction is made in QRUS between parts and labor. *Parts:* Maintenance costs for Truck III of QRUS on paved roads amount to 0.2 percent of the depreciable value of the vehicle per 1,000 kms. The same percentage was taken for both the two-axle and three-axle trucks. For Truck III of QRUS on paved roads *labor* costs per 1,000 kms amounted to 3.76 hours of labor. This was also used for the trucks in Iran. Maintenance costs on gravel and earth roads were calculated on the basis of the cost on paved roads in combination with the appropriate conversion factors mentioned in QRUS.

Maintenance Costs, Trucks

	Parts	*(per 1,000 kms)* Labor
	(as percentage of depreciable value of the vehicle)	*(hours of labor)*
On paved roads	0.12	3.76
On gravel roads	0.18	5.64
On earth roads	0.30	9.40

Time Costs

For the passenger cars, as in QRUS,[7] an occupancy of 1.8 persons was assumed. Although the occupancy rate in Iran on the highways

---

[6] The relationship between speed and annual mileage (QRUS, p. 60, para. 38 and p. 62, Annex Chart I–A) is:

Speed	*Annual Mileage ('000 kms)*
72	100.0
56	77.6
48	66.7

[7] QRUS, p. 72, paras. 57 and 58; also Table 9, p. 25.

119

is, no doubt, much higher,[8] for a fair percentage of the number of occupants (women, children, friends) no real time costs are involved. For the trucks, one driver plus one assistant per truck has been considered representative.[9]

Road User Savings including Taxes

In connection with the analysis of the relationship between rate reduction and road user savings (see Chapter VI), the table below presents the road user savings calculated at 1960 prices, including taxes.

ANNEX TABLE 7: Road User Savings, at 1960 Prices, including Taxes

(rials per 1,000 kms)

	Improvement from Gravel to Paved Road	
	Two-axle truck	Three-axle truck
Fuel	166	194
Engine Oil	16	18
Tire Wear	740	1,476
Depreciation	267	453
Interest	137	232
Maintenance (parts)	589	996
Maintenance (labor)	188	188
Driver/assistant	345	345
Total	2,448	3,902
Total, in rials per capacity ton-km	.23	.26

Comparison with Other Estimates

To conclude this section dealing with road user costs and savings, the savings estimates in this study are compared with estimates from the original appraisal report of May 1959, and those from a recent appraisal report of a road project in Iran (February 1964). The order of magnitude of the original estimate of 1959 is roughly in line with this study, but the estimates of 1964 seem to be low.

---

[8] On the basis of a small sample (24 cars consecutively observed on the Iranian highways in the spring of 1965) the authors calculated an average occupancy rate of between 4 and 5 persons per car.

[9] QRUS, p. 72, para. 58, indicates 1.2 persons on the average; for the relationship between speed and travelling time, see QRUS, Table 9, p. 25.

ANNEX TABLE 8: Road User Savings per Capacity Ton-km, excluding Taxes

(rials)

	Appraisal Report 1959 (1)	Appraisal Report 1964 (2)	This Study[a] (3)	
		Two-axle 10 ton	Two-axle 10.5 ton	Three-axle 15 ton
Type of truck:				
Road Improvement from				
Earth to gravel		.21	.41	.49
Gravel to paved		.16	.22	.25
Earth to paved	.45	.37	.63	.73

[a] See Table 20, p. 55.

Average Trucking Costs and Rates

The information obtained on the typical trucking costs of a medium-sized firm with fifty trucks, mainly operating on good and well-maintained highways in Iran, is shown in detail in Annex Table 9. The cost data refer again to a two-axle 10.5 ton truck and a three-axle 15 ton truck, the two predominant types in Iran. The calculations are based on data reflecting the joint knowledge of three experts in the trucking field in Iran.[10] Confirmation of the results came from other independent sources—the National Iranian Oil Company, a transport firm, two truck importers, a tire manufacturer, and two firms having their own trucking fleet (a soft drink manufacturer and a liquid gas producer and distributor). This general consensus, with only minor departures, inspired confidence in the data presented in Annex Table 9, even where they diverge considerably from widely held views. In particular, there was general agreement on the exceptionally long twenty-year lifetime of the trucks, on the annual vehicle mileage and the lifetime tire mileage.[11]

---

[10] The questionnaire used for this purpose was adapted from Economic Commission for Europe Inland Transportation Committee, Working Party on Transport Costs, *Document No. W/Trans/WP26/94*, (May 15, 1951).

[11] With annual mileage about 30 percent lower, a twenty-year vehicle life indicates a lifetime mileage roughly twice as high as indicated in QRUS (see p. 60, Trucks III and IV). For tires, for the three-axle truck, one of the interviewees quoted a rule of thumb of "a tire a month." This ties in with the annual mileage of the truck (75,000 kms), the lifetime mileage of a tire (60,000 kms) and the number of tires per vehicle (10).

ANNEX TABLE 9: Average Year-Round Trucking Costs, Iran, 1965[a]

1. *Types of truck:*

Two-axle, 6 wheel truck, net weight		8
	load capacity	10.5 tons
	gross vehicle weight	18.5 tons
Three-axle, 10 wheel truck, net weight		12 tons
	load capacity	15 tons
	gross vehicle weight	27 tons

2. *Size of the average trucking firm:*
50 trucks (25 two-axle, 25 three-axle)

3. *Annual cost per truck by cost category:*

(a) Fuel costs

	Two-axle truck	Three-axle truck
diesel oil consumption per 100 kms	50 liters	65 liters
annually travelled distance	75,000 kms	75,000 kms
annual fuel consumption	37,500 liters	48,750 liters
price of 1 liter of diesel oil	2.5 rials	2.5 rials
annual fuel consumption costs	93,750 rials	121,875 rials

(b) Lubricating oil costs

oil consumption per 100 kms	2 liters	2.5 liters
annually travelled distance	75,000 kms	75,000 kms
annual oil consumption	1,500 liters	1,875 liters
price of 1 liter of oil	18 rials	18 rials
annual oil consumption costs	27,000 rials	33,750 rials

(c) Tire costs

tires per vehicle	6	10
tire life	60,000 kms	60,000 kms
annually travelled distance	75,000 kms	75,000 kms
number of tires consumed per year	7.5	12.5
price of 1 tire	10,000 rials	12,000 rials
annual tire costs	75,000 rials	150,000 rials

(d) Depreciation costs

	Two-axle truck	Three-axle truck
new value of trucks	1,150,000 rials	1,950,000 rials
lifetime of trucks	20 years	20 years
annual depreciation	57,500 rials	97,500 rials

(e) Interest

average value of truck (50%)	575,000 rials	975,000 rials
10% of average value	57,500 rials	97,500 rials

(f) Maintenance costs

annual costs	150,000 rials	150,000 rials

[a] Costs of the trucker (i.e. including all duties, levies, taxes, etc.) for operation of trucks on well-paved roads.

(g)	Driver's and assistant's costs (rials)		
	monthly driver's wage	10,000	10,000
	monthly assistant's wage	4,500	4,500
	annual driver's wage	120,000	120,000
	annual assistant's wage	54,000	54,000
	annual wages of crew	175,000	174,000

(h)	Overhead costs	
	annual overhead costs of the firm	1,000,000 rials
	number of trucks	50
	annual overhead costs per truck	20,000 rials

(i)	Summary of annual year-round costs of trucking (rials)		
	(a) fuel	93,750	121,880
	(b) lubricating oil	27,000	33,750
	(c) tires	75,000	150,000
	(d) depreciation	57,500	97,500
	(e) interest	57,500	97,500
	(f) maintenance	150,000	150,000
	(g) driver plus assistant	174,000	174,000
	(h) overhead	20,000	20,000

4.	*Total costs per vehicle-km:*		
	Total annual cost	654,750 rials	844,630 rials
	Annually travelled distance	75,000 kms	75,000 kms
	Total costs per vehicle-km	8.73 rials	11.26 rials

5.	*Total costs per capacity ton-km:*		
	Total costs per vehicle-km	8.73 rials	11.26 rials
	Ton capacity per vehicle	10.5 tons	15.0 tons
	Total costs per capacity ton-km	.83 rials	.75 rials

Sources: Private truckers, weighing stations, tire manufacturer, truck importers.

The average year-round trucking costs per vehicle-km in Iran are thus estimated at Rials 8.73 and 11.26 for two- and three-axle trucks respectively.

It is interesting to try to reconcile these year-round trucking costs, derived from operating truckers in Iran, with the road user costs for trucks on paved roads shown in Table 21, p. 58, and derived largely from the basic data in QRUS.

Type of Truck	Average Year-round Trucking Costs	Road User Costs Trucks
	(*on paved roads, rials per vehicle-km*)	
Two-axle, 10.5 ton	8.73	4.80
Three-axle, 15 ton	11.26	6.96

They are about 60–80 percent higher. This gap reflects the different nature of the two cost concepts. First, the year-round trucking cost figures include taxes, while the road user cost estimates do not; if the road user costs are recalculated on the basis of 1965 prices, including taxes, they increase by about 15–17 percent. Second, the road user costs assume a specific speed for trucks on paved roads of 72 kms per hour. The year-round trucking costs, however, imply an average annual road speed that is 25 percent lower, i.e. 54 kms per hour.[12] This difference in speed is reflected in the calculation of several cost items, such as depreciation and interest, which go down with higher annual road speed. The speed factor, for these two cost items, raises year-round trucking costs by another 7–9 percent over road user costs. Other factors relating to the specific conditions governing the road user costs are best illustrated by the wage costs for the driver and assistant. They do not drive eight hours every day and, when they drive, not constantly at 72 kms per hour. The difference in wage costs adds another 23 percent (for two-axle trucks) or 16 percent (for three-axle trucks) to the road user costs. Fourth, overhead costs are included in the year-round trucking cost calculations, but excluded from road user costs. This explains 6 percent (for two-axle trucks) or 3 percent (for three-axle trucks) of higher year-round costs.

The factors above explain about two-thirds to three-quarters of the difference between the year-round trucking costs and the road user costs. Other factors that tend to make the year-round trucking costs higher than the road user costs are less easily quantified. For example, year-round trucking costs, but not the road user costs as here defined, are affected by braking, stopping with idling motor (urban traffic), and ups and downs and curvature of the road.[13] On

---

[12] QRUS, p. 60, para. 38.

[13] For the impact of the rate of rise and fall and the curvature of the road on fuel consumption, see QRUS Table 3b–ii, p. 16, and Table 3c–iii, p. 18. For Truck III, for example, rate and rise and fall of 2 meters per 100 meters increases fuel consumption by 54 percent; and 6 degrees of curvature would add another 10 percent. Similarly, tire wear on a curved road is higher than on a straight road. The relatively large difference between the engine oil component in road user costs and in year-round trucking costs seems only explainable in part by the above factors. Because the engine oil consumption in the road user cost calculation was based on Truck III of QRUS (gasoline engine), some underestimation is probably involved. Truck IV of QRUS (diesel engine), only slightly heavier than Truck III, consumes about twice as much.

balance, it seems safe to conclude from this comparison that the road user costs calculated in this study are reasonably realistic and possibly on the low side.

Average Trucking Rates and Profits

A comparison was also attempted between year-round trucking costs and average trucking rates. As discussed in Chapter VI, p. 60, the rate on the Khoramshahr–Tehran route was, during 1961–65, some Rials 1.35 per ton-km. Rates on other routes proved hard to obtain, in the absence of (effective) central rate-making bodies as the Khoramshahr Trucking Syndicate. Available data are given in Annex Table 10. The southbound rate between Tehran and Khoramshahr is very much lower than the northbound, as would be expected, given that more than twice as large a volume of commodities is transported northbound. Other rates tend to fall between the extreme high and low on the major traffic route, Khoramshahr–Tehran.

ANNEX TABLE 10: Truck Rates between Various Towns, 1965

From	To	Commodity	Rials per ton-km	Source
Tehran	Khoramshahr	Not specified	.27– .45	1,2
Mashad	Tehran	Hay, cattle fodder	.55	1
Shiraz	Tehran	Not specified	.65– .87	2
Tehran	Mashad	Not specified	.72– .99	1
Kermanshah	Tehran	Not specified	.76–1.33	2
Shiraz	Bandar Shahpoor	Not specified	.78– .97	2
Rasht	Tehran[a]	Rice	.87	3
Kermanshah	Hamadan	Not specified	1.05	2
Khoramshahr	Tehran	Average	1.35	4
Shiraz	Bushire	Not specified	.84–1.67	2

[a] 1964, dry months; cold season up to Rials 1.90 per ton-km.

Sources: 1. Kayhan Journal, (Tehran, April 8, 1965).
2. Based on interviews in Hamadan, Kermanshah, Shiraz, Tehran.
3. H. S. Lodi, Report on Marketing of Rice in Safid Rud Dam Area, p. 5, (Tehran, 1964).
4. Table 22, p. 59.

The data give a rough idea of trucking rates in Iran. Taking the main traffic artery, Khoramshahr–Tehran, as a yardstick, and allowing for the greater tonnage flowing north than south, the average rate on the round trip between Khoramshahr and Tehran is about Rial 1. This average rate per ton-km is, of course, not directly comparable to the year-round average trucking costs of Rial 0.75–0.83

per *capacity* ton-km shown in Annex Table 9. Trucking profits will depend on the average load factor.

This is illustrated below, for two rates per ton-km on the Tehran–Khoramshahr route (see Annex Table 10) and for varying load factors on that route. The load factor, and the rate per ton-km on the Khoramshahr–Tehran route, are kept constant at 100 percent and Rials 1.35, throughout. Average cost per capacity-ton km are assumed to be Rial 0.79. Annex Table 11 shows that at a rate of Rial 0.27 per ton-km on the Tehran–Khoramshahr route, the load factor on that route (given the above assumptions) would need to be as high as 85 percent for truckers to break even on a round trip journey. At a rate of Rial 0.45 on the Tehran–Khoramshahr route, truckers would still break even with a load factor, more realistically, as low as 50 percent.[14] Small differences in the average costs, or in the

ANNEX TABLE 11:   Relationship of Load Factor to Profit

Load Factor Tehran–Khoramshahr (*percent*)	Average Round Trip Rate (*rials per ton-km*)		Round Trip Revenue (*rials per capacity ton-km*)		Round Trip Profit	
	A	B	A	B	A	B
100	.81	.90	.81	.90	.020	.110
95	.824	.912	.803	.889	.013	.099
90	.838	.924	.797	.878	.007	.088
80	.870	.950	.783	.855		.065
70	.905	.979	.770	.833		.093
60	.945	1.013	.756	.810		.020
50	.990	1.050	.743	.788		

Note: A: On the basis of a Tehran-Khoramshahr rate of Rial 0.27 per ton-km (see Annex Table 10);
B: On the basis of a Tehran-Khoramshahr rate of Rial 0.45 per ton-km; Khoramshahr–Tehran route: load factor 100 percent; rate Rials 1.35 per ton-km. Average trucking costs per capacity ton-km, Rial 0.79.

---

[14] On the basis of the weighing station information it is impossible to arrive at a firm conclusion as to the average load factor of southbound truck traffic. There is uncertainty not only about the number of fully loaded southbound trucks (see Annex I), but even more about the number of partly loaded southbound trucks and their average load. If it is accepted that the southbound flow of freight is appreciably smaller than the northbound flow, it is plausible to assume that the southbound flow will comprise a significant proportion of partly loaded trucks. A comparison therefore of the northbound and southbound flows on the basis of fully loaded trucks would tend to underestimate systematically the relative significance of the southbound flow of freight.

Khoramshahr–Tehran rate, can be analyzed similarly.[15] It is clear that the profits (or losses) of the truckers are sensitive to small changes in rates, costs, or load factors. The analysis also suggests that the cost and rate figures in this study are broadly consistent.

A comparison of the year-round trucking costs (excluding taxes), according to this study, with similar data from the 1959 and 1964 project appraisal reports, shows the latter estimates to be considerably higher. Taking into account the load factor and taxes, they appear out of line with the general trucking rate level in Iran.

Year-Round Trucking Costs (excluding taxes)

	Appraisal Report 1959 (1)	Appraisal Report 1964 (2)	This Study 1965[a] (3)	
	(rials per capacity ton-km on paved road)			
Type of truck	—	Two-axle 10 ton	Two-axle 10.5 ton	Three-axle 15 ton
	1.05	1.04	.74	.66

[a] See Table 21, p. 58.

---

[15] It should be noted that the average rate per ton-km (not, of course, revenue per *capacity*-ton km) goes up with lower load factors on the Tehran-Khoramshahr route, where rates are much lower than northbound.